RECOVERY STRATEGIES 4 LIFE

Student Workbook

Unit 1

Relationship With God

Developed By:

Paula Mosher Wallace
Ginny Priz, CPLC
Evonna Surrette, MA, LPC

Published by Bloom Publishing, an imprint of Bloom In The Dark, Inc.

Recovery Strategies 4 Life Unit 1 Student Workbook: Relationship with God
Paperback edition, Published September 20, 2019

Cover Design: Ginny Priz
Editing: Jean Przyborowski

ISBN-13: 978-0-9965309-4-1
ISBN-10: 0-9965309-4-0

Bloominthedark.org
RS4L.com

Scripture references are limited quotes from the online versions of these Bibles:
New International Version
King James Version
New King James Version

Table of Contents

About the Content Developers/Instructors .... *vii*

Introduction .... *ix*

Disclaimer .... *xi*

Week 1: What To Expect

LISTENING GUIDE 1

DISCUSSION QUESTIONS 5

Building Your Support System Worksheet 6

Week 2: Saying Hello to Reality

LISTENING GUIDE 9

DISCUSSION QUESTIONS 15

Saying Hello to Reality (Denial) Worksheet 16

Life Events Assessment 21

Week 3: Fantasy Versus Reality

LISTENING GUIDE 31

DISCUSSION QUESTIONS 37

What Healing/Recovery Looks Like for Me Worksheet 38

Week 4: Who God Is

LISTENING GUIDE 47

DISCUSSION QUESTIONS 51

Who God Made You to Be Worksheet 52

Who I Am Scriptures 54

Who God Is Scriptures 55

Week 5: God's Heart for Restoration

LISTENING GUIDE 57

DISCUSSION QUESTIONS 59

What's Broken Needs Healing Worksheet 60

Physical Health Family Tree Exercise 62

Week 6: The Love of Father God
    LISTENING GUIDE 67

    DISCUSSION QUESTIONS 73

Loving Father Description Worksheet 74

The Love of The Father Scriptures 78

Father's Repentance and Blessing Exercise 80

Week 7: Surrender to God
    LISTENING GUIDE 83

    DISCUSSION QUESTIONS 89

Armor of God Scripture Exercise 90

Create Worship Playlist Worksheet 91

Worship Playlist 93

Week 8: Positive Coping Tools
    LISTENING GUIDE 95

    DISCUSSION QUESTIONS 103

Comprehensive Action Plan Worksheet 104

Emotional Survival Kit 107

Self Care Guide Worksheet 108

Week 9: Progression of Sin
    LISTENING GUIDE 113

    DISCUSSION QUESTIONS 117

Taking Thoughts Captive Worksheet 118

Week 10: Cognitive Distortions
    LISTENING GUIDE 123

    DISCUSSION QUESTIONS 129

Cognitive Distortions Worksheet 131

Mental Health Family Tree Exercise 132

Week 11: You Are NOT Your Emotions

LISTENING GUIDE 137

DISCUSSION QUESTIONS 141

Toxic Versus Safe Worksheet 142

Unit 1 Assessment 145

Appendix A: Life Events Assessment Answer Key 151

Appendix B: Who We Are Scripture List 162

Appendix C: Who God Is Scripture List 163

Appendix D: The Serenity Prayer 165

Appendix E: Hotlines 166

Appendix F: Additional Resources 169

Appendix G: Bloom Forward Morning Sheet 170

Appendix H: Bloom Forward Evening Sheet 171

Appendix I: Father's Repentance and Blessing 172

Appendix J: Mother's Repentance and Blessing 174

Appendix K: Spiritual Leader's Repentance and Blessing 176

Appendix L: Worship Playlist 178

Appendix M: Armor of God Scripture 179

Appendix N: Suggestions for Self Care 181

Appendix O: RS4L Strategies 183

Appendix P: Listening Guide Answer Keys 187

About Bloom In The Dark, Inc. 191

Watch Bloom Today TV Around the World 192

Our Books 193

About the Content Developers/Instructors

Paula Mosher Wallace
President of Bloom In The Dark, Inc.

Born in the jungles of Peru to missionary parents, Paula began life saturated in the Word of God. With Bible classes as part of every school year plus 4 years of Bible college, Paula's knowledge of the Truth grew. An Ex-Victim of abuse, Paula became the author and founder of Bloom In The Dark. She also produces and co-hosts Bloom Today, an international TV show discussing abuse. In RS4L, Paula teaches Biblical recovery, highlighting God's heart for healing the broken.

paula@bloominthedark.com | 478-335-3910

Ginny Priz
Certified Professional Life Coach

Being born with her right arm stopping just below the elbow taught Ginny to trust God's plan. But her recovery journey from codependency, alcohol, & panic attacks taught her to trust God with the deep, broken parts of her heart - one moment at a time. To help other women find this freedom, Ginny became a certified Christian life coach, speaker, and author of Ditch The Drama. She also anchors Bloom Today, a Christian talk show broadcast in over 200 countries.

ginny@bloominthedark.com | ginnypriz.com

Evonna Surrette, MA, LPC
Trauma & Attachment Therapist

Evonna's life passion is to provide hope and healing to those who suffer from trauma, attachment, eating, and mood disorders. As an Ex-Victim of trauma and eating disorders, Evonna has extensive professional experience in working with trauma, attachment, and a wide range of mental health issues. Evonna has over a decade in ministry and leadership. Evonna takes a holistic approach (spirit, soul, & body) as she believes in removing the roots, not just treating the symptoms.

refinedhope.com

Introduction

1 Thessalonians 5:23 NKJV
"Now may the God of peace Himself sanctify you completely; and may your
whole spirit, soul, and body be preserved blameless at the coming of our Lord
Jesus Christ."

Welcome to Recovery Strategies 4 Life (RS4L)! We are excited to have you be a part of this program. Unlike traditional recovery programs that only address the soul and body, RS4L combines healing strategies for all three parts of our being: spirit, soul, and body.

The purpose of this course is to disciple and equip leaders and individuals who have experienced brokenness through their healing/recovery journey by applying proven strategies to their lives.

This one-year course will completely transform how you see healing/recovery and will equip you with powerful tools to help you heal so that you can effectively help those around you.

At the completion of the course, you will:
1. Understand that each of us is a triune being made of a spirit, soul, and body, that we can be wounded in all three areas and healing is needed in all three.
2. Have the ability to identify damaging habits or compulsive behaviors and replace them with positive coping skills.
3. Create and foster meaningful, healthy relationships with others.
4. Surrender your will to God, seek His will, and obey His will on a daily basis.
5. Own your identity in Christ and all that God designed you to be.
6. Develop a healthy support system including a sponsor, accountability partners, recovery support group(s), church, counselor and/or life coach.
7. Understand how the physical and spiritual realms influence each other on the battlefield of the mind, and how to win the battle using a custom-made, detailed plan.
8. Understand the impact of spiritual warfare in daily life, the strategies and tactics of Satan, and how to fight enemy attacks.
9. Be able to identify your needs and practice self care.
10. Identify where trauma, loss, or stressful events may have wounded you and develop a healthy approach to processing difficult emotions and events.
11. Identify destructive core beliefs and replace them with God's truth.
12. Have the ability to use RS4L materials to lead others through their healing/recovery journey.

Please email us at paula@bloominthedark.com or ginny@bloominthedark.com with any questions, confusion, suggestions, or feedback.

Disclaimer

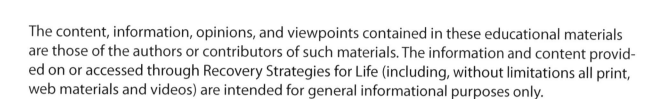

The content, information, opinions, and viewpoints contained in these educational materials are those of the authors or contributors of such materials. The information and content provided on or accessed through Recovery Strategies for Life (including, without limitations all print, web materials and videos) are intended for general informational purposes only.

The information and materials provide on or accessed through Recovery Strategies for Life program are intended solely for individuals seeking information about healing for the spirit, soul and body, and are not intended for individuals seeking medical advice or treatment. The instructors and contributors are sharing their personal testimonies of healing. Accordingly, the information and materials presented are not intended nor implied to be a substitute for professional medical advice, diagnosis or treatment. Any individual always should seek the advice of a physician or other qualified healthcare provider prior to starting any new treatment, selecting a method of treatment, or seeking answers to any questions regarding a medical or mental health condition. Nothing contained or accessed through this program is intended to be and should not be used for medical diagnosis or treatment. Participants and leaders of this program should never disregard professional medical advice, mental health advice, or delay in seeking treatment based on the information contained in this program.

The information and education material contained herein is meant to promote the general understanding and dialog of healing spirit, soul and body. Such information is not meant or intended to serve as a substitute for any healthcare professional's clinical training, experience, or judgment. For participants, such information is not to be a substitute for professional medical, therapeutic, or healthcare advice or counseling. For medical issues or concerns, including decisions about medications and other treatments, participants should always consult their physician or, in serious cases, seek immediate assistance from emergency personnel.

If you are a mental health care professional, you should rely on your professional judgment in evaluating any and all information, and confirm the information contained in this program with other sources and reliable third parties before undertaking any treatment based on it. If you are a consumer or patient, you should evaluate the information together with your physician or another qualified healthcare professional. The instructors and content developers make no warranty that the information contained herein will be error free, and the readers of such information use such at their own risk.

Week 1

What To Expect

LISTENING GUIDE

You are not alone! All three of us - Ginny, Evonna, and Paula - have walked through past seasons of incredible hurts. You'll learn a little about our journeys today, and a lot more about them in the weeks to come.

Rest assured, we'll walk you through this "all inclusive" healing process one step at a time, one strategy at a time toward healing for your spirit, soul, and body.

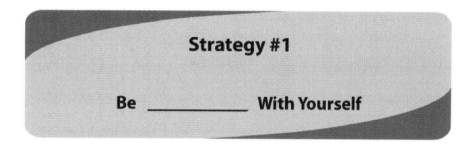

Strategy #1

Be _____ With Yourself

The only person who can address your issues is you. It starts with intentionally looking inward.

Painful emotions may arise when you start to get honest, but it also opens the door to joy and love and happiness as well. Numbing our emotions or distracting ourselves from focusing on emotions will leave us hurting even more.

NOTES

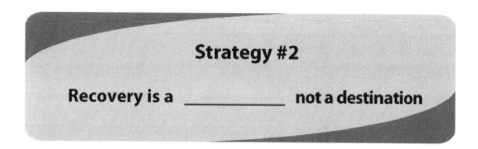

Strategy #2

Recovery is a _____ not a destination

Take it one day at a time, or even one moment at a time, like it says in the Serenity Prayer.

This is a process that happens over time. You did not learn your old perspectives and coping skills in a day, and it will take time to adopt new perspectives and coping skills.

This is a lifestyle and not a quick fix! There is no such thing as a quick fix.

Give yourself lots of grace! This is not a precise, easy process. Expect there to be some messy times as you grow and make changes. There is nothing wrong with these times; they can actually be very healing! Just don't plan to stay there in the mess – keep going to the other side.

We do not fight against flesh and blood. (Ephesians 6:12) The enemy works by trying to stir up heightened emotions, confusion, and chaos. Do not be discouraged or afraid! This is an indication you are on the right track and doing as God has asked. You are important enough for the enemy to feel threatened by your healing!

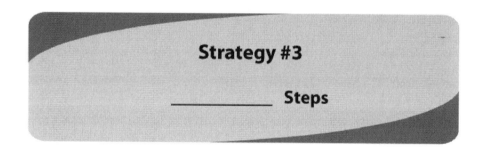

Strategy #3

_____ Steps

Slow down. Take the time you need to soak up new concepts and apply them.

To get the most out of this journey, be thorough and fully work through each of the steps, exercises, and strategies. They build on each other. By applying any of them at a surface level, you will only make the process more difficult for yourself.

Healing can be tiring. Focusing on just one little piece at a time each week will help you from taking on too much or becoming overwhelmed. You'll "eat the elephant" by the end of this course, but only if you eat it "one bite at a time!"

NOTES

WEEKLY WORSHIP
"Freedom Hymn" by Austin French

DISCUSSION QUESTIONS

1. Why did you decide to take this course?

2. What do you hope to get out of this program?

3. Out of the 3 strategies given in this lesson, which do you think will be the biggest challenge for you and why?
    1. Be Honest with Yourself
    2. Recovery is a Journey not a Destination
    3. Baby Steps

Building Your Support System Worksheet
Week 1 Homework

Begin by praying. Ask God to walk you through the process of recognizing and asking a support team to partner with you on this healing journey. *(If the following questions don't help you develop a team list, ask God to connect you to those He has prepared to help you.)*

1. Consider the people you live with. Do you have anyone who would be safe to support you in this recovery journey? Who? (If you live alone or don't have anyone in your home who's safe to help you, don't be discouraged. Many other options are available.)

2. Consider the people you work with. Do you have a friend who would support you along your healing journey? Who?

3. Consider who you go to church with. Do you have a pastor, small group leader, or friends to share this journey with? Who?

4. Consider your neighbors. Do you have a neighbor you trust who would be willing to support you? Who?

5. Are you part of a recovery group already? If so, which one? Do you have a sponsor? (Recovery groups are a great place to find support regardless of your hurt, habit or hang-up.)

6. Have you worked with a counselor or coach in the past? Are you working with one now? If not, consider the added value that working with a professional during this process would bring.

7. Who will you ask to join you on this journey? From the first six questions, make a list of 5 or 6 people who you will ask to walk with you through this process. Write their names down, and then ask them during this week.

Week 2

Saying Hello to Reality

LISTENING GUIDE

> ## Strategy #4
>
> Healthy _____ System

Component #1: _____

Find people with whom it's okay to be open and honest. People who are accepting of your struggle and not shaming.

Those who point you to God and the Bible for answers rather than their own opinions can help you nurture a healthy relationship with God.

No one else can play the role of God in your life. If a person or group is consistently wanting you to look to them for answers rather than God, that is a red flag! Cults come in all kinds of forms.

NOTES

Component #2: _____

Sponsor/Mentor – This is someone who is ahead of you in the healing process and can help give you guidance in the journey. They should be of the same sex and have gone through similar struggles as you. This way, they can celebrate with you when you are on the right track, and give instructions and guidance when you need to get back on track.

Accountability Partners – These folks are just about in the same place along the healing journey with you. Consider the people in your RS4L group (if you are participating with a group) as your partners. This is more of a 2-way street relationship than the top-down sponsor/ mentor relationship. We recommend asking at least 2-3 people to be your accountability partners. Be open to sharing and listening to each other regularly. This works best when partners have permission to speak life and warnings where you may not see clearly. Others can see more from the outside than you can see from the inside. This is true for all of us.

Spiritual Covering – Prayer is powerful! Ask someone who walks closely with God to be praying for you and interceding for you. This could be someone at your church or a friend or a group of friends. Examine the fruit in their lives first, and if it is in line with God's heart, their roots will be in Christ.

If you do not have people in your life right now that you feel comfortable asking to fill these roles, then ask God to lead you to the right people. He knows what you need and He will direct your path.

Component #3: _____

Hotlines – A list of free hotlines can be found in the appendices of this student workbook.

Recovery Programs – These can be anything from 12 Step Anonymous programs to Celebrate Recovery, Support Groups, or Church groups. These are groups where everyone in the group is actively addressing and focused on healing from a wound, addiction, etc. -preferably a group that is struggling with the same issue as yourself.

Professionals – There is nothing wrong with seeking help from professionals including doctors, counselors, life coaches, or pastors. These can be tools in your tool box that are extremely targeted – they can address your personal needs with personalized help.

Question #1: Where do I feel _____?

Are you able to make changes and improvements in some areas of your life, but in others you keep hitting the same impossible hurdles? Those are often the places where you're getting stuck.

Maybe you want to choose a different kind of relationship, behavior, or perspective, but you can't seem to make any progress no matter how hard you try.

NOTES

Question #2: Do I have recurring _____?

If the same hurts are coming up repeatedly in your life, you may have an old wound that keeps getting stepped on. Rather than blaming everyone who steps on the old wound, it might be time to recognize that your sensitivity is causing the emotional upheaval.

If you are a victim of abuse, that abuse was never your fault.

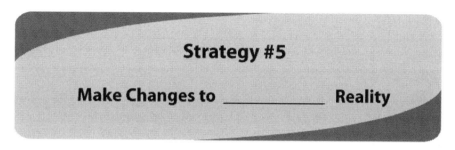

Strategy #5

Make Changes to _____ Reality

Consequence #1: _____ us from God, ourselves, and others.

Denial separates us and disconnects us from God, ourselves and others. There will always be a piece of our soul that will be withheld from our interactions as long as we are in denial.

Consequence #2: _____ our feelings.

Denial disables our feelings so they are stuffed or entirely shut down. The problem is you cannot stuff only one kind of feeling. If you try to shut down one feeling – such as fear or anger or hurt – positive feelings will also be stuffed or shut down as well. It is not healthy for our spirit, soul, or body.

Consequence #3: Keeps us stuck and stops _____.

Denial keeps us stuck. It stops our emotional growth in that area. Chemical use, shutting down or stuffing our emotions, ignoring people or entire chunks of our past, will keep us stuck on a soul level. Over time, that soul wound will negatively affect our spirit and physical bodies as well.

Suggestions to help you come out of denial:
- Asking for feedback in one area of your life from a safe, trusted person (or persons) is one way you can come out of denial and begin to address your blind spots with God.

- Ask God to reveal which area of denial, if any, He'd like to show you first.

- Ask a trusted pastor or spiritual leader, or reach out to Bloom In The Dark to find out how you can deepen your relationship with God.

NOTES

WEEKLY WORSHIP
"No Longer Slaves" by Bethel

DISCUSSION QUESTIONS

1. Do you already have a healthy support system? If so, who makes up that support system? If not, what do you feel will be your biggest obstacle in creating one?

2. Facing reality is hard – what area of life did God speak to your heart about during the videos that you need to address? (What are you in denial about?)

3. Are there any areas that others have pointed out to you, but you just can't seem to agree with them?

Saying Hello to Reality (Denial) Worksheet
Week 2 Homework

The following questions are designed to help you think through the areas in your life that you want to make changes in during this year. Be honest. Ask God to show you His views in these areas. If you are struggling to answer these questions ask a safe friend or counselor who knows you to help you.

1. What areas of your life are you hoping to improve? Be specific.

2. What areas in your life do you feel in control of? Be specific.

3. What areas in your life do you feel are out of control? Be specific.

4. In what areas of your life do you feel stuck? Be specific.

5. What family secrets have you felt responsible to stay quiet about?

6. What personal secrets have you needed to hide?

7. List the things that – if they had been different – would have made your life much better.

8. What are you constantly worrying about? Be specific.

9. What are some reasons that pride has kept you from reaching out for help to overcome the struggles you've faced?

10. What did you do in your childhood to cope with the problems in your life? To protect yourself? To get attention?

11. What do you do to handle hurt or disappointment now?

12. What have you done to cope with or escape from emotional pain or discomfort? Be specific.

13. How did your choices in the last 3 questions negatively affect you?

14. What do you feel is keeping you separated from God, others or yourself?

15. What unrealistic expectations have you placed on God, others or yourself?

Life Events Assessment

The purpose of this assessment is to help you understand the significant, painful life events that have contributed to the physical, emotional, and spiritual wounds on your journey.

The type and frequency of painful events that you have experienced will impact the length and complexity of your recovery and healing journey.

A key to scoring your assessment can be found in the appendices.

LOSS

1. Have you ever experienced a significant loss that affected you physically, emotionally or spiritually?
    Yes
    No
2. Have you ever experienced losing a job that caused emotional/spiritual pain?
    Yes
    No
3. Have you ever experienced the loss of a loved one, a close friend, and/or romantic partner?
    Yes
    No
    a. Was it a sudden death?
        Yes
        No
    b. Did they die by suicide?
        Yes
        No
    c. Was it a violent death?
        Yes
        No
4. Have you ever experienced the death of a child?
    Yes
    No
5. Have you ever experienced the loss of a child to addiction, incarceration, abduction etc.?
    Yes
    No

6. Have you ever experienced a miscarriage?
    Yes
    No
7. Have you ever experienced delivering a stillborn?
    Yes
    No
8. Have you ever been divorced?
    Yes
    No
9. Have you ever had an abortion?
    Yes
    No

STRESSFUL LIFE EVENTS
1. Have you ever had a life threatening illness (physical or mental)?
    Yes
    No
2. Do you currently struggle with a chronic illness?
    Yes
    No
3. Have you ever been in a life threatening accident?
    Yes
    No
    a. Did anyone die in that accident?
        Yes
        No
    b. Did you sustain serious injuries?
        Yes
        No
4. Have you ever been robbed or mugged?
    Yes
    No
    a. Was physical force or a weapon used?
        Yes
        No
    b. Did you sustain injuries from the event?
        Yes
        No
5. Have you ever been in military combat or a war zone?
    Yes
    No

6. Have you ever witnessed sexual or physical violence?

        Yes

        No

    a. Did it occur before the age 10?

            Yes

            No

    b. Did it occur between the ages 10-20?

            Yes

            No

    c. Did it occur after age 20?

            Yes

            No

7. Have you ever witnessed mass violence (riots, shootings, fires, accidents, bombings, etc.)?

        Yes

        No

    a. Did it occur before age 10?

            Yes

            No

    b. Did it occur between the ages 10-20?

            Yes

            No

    c. Did it occur after age 20?

            Yes

            No

8. Have you ever witnessed a traumatic natural disaster?

        Yes

        No

9. Have you ever been extremely frightened or horrified, felt helpless or traumatized by a situation that has not been referenced above?

        Yes

        No

10. Have you ever been arrested or been incarcerated?

        Yes

        No

11. Have you ever been in foster care or were you adopted?

        Yes

        No

12. Have you ever lived with anyone who was a problem drinker or alcoholic, and/or used drugs?

> Yes
>
> No

    a. If you were a child, were your parents too drunk or high to take care of you or take you to the doctor if needed?

> > Yes
> >
> > No

13. As a child did you ever feel that you didn't have enough to eat, had to wear dirty clothing and/or had no one to protect you?

> Yes
>
> No

TRAUMA

1. Have you ever experienced being punched, slapped in the face, hit excessively, kicked, pinned down or otherwise physically attacked or harmed by someone?

> Yes
>
> No

    a. Did it occur before age 10?

> > Yes
> >
> > No

    b. Did it occur between the ages 10-20?

> > Yes
> >
> > No

    c. Did it occur after age 20?

> > Yes
> >
> > No

    d. Did you sustain injuries?

> > Yes
> >
> > No

    e. Was it by a spouse or romantic partner?

> > Yes
> >
> > No

2. Have you ever experienced being repeatedly ridiculed, put down, ignored or told you were worthless, had no value or otherwise verbally attacked or demeaned?

> Yes
>
> No

    a. Did it occur during ages 0-10?

> > Yes
> >
> > No

    b. Did it occur during ages 10-20?

> > Yes
> >
> > No

    c. Did it occur during ages 20 plus?
        Yes
        No
    d. Was it by a spouse or romantic partner?
        Yes
        No

3. Have you ever experienced someone attempting to control or manipulate your emotions by dismissing your feelings, by convincing you your feelings are wrong or improper by making threats etc.?
        Yes
        No
    a. Did it occur before age 10?
        Yes
        No
    b. Did it occur between the ages 10-20?
        Yes
        No
    c. Did it occur after age 20?
        Yes
        No
    d. Was it by a spouse or romantic partner?
        Yes
        No

4. Have you ever experienced being physically forced to have intercourse, oral or anal sex against your wishes (even if you were asleep, intoxicated or married to them)?
        Yes
        No
    a. Did it occur before age 10?
        Yes
        No
    b. Did it occur between the ages 10-20?
        Yes
        No
    c. Did it occur after age 20?
        Yes
        No
    d. Was it same gender?
        Yes
        No

5. Have you ever experienced being touched or forced/coerced to touch others inappropriately in private areas (over or under clothing)?

      Yes

      No

   a. Did it occur before age 10?

      Yes

      No

   b. Did it occur between the ages 10-20?

      Yes

      No

   c. Did it occur after age 20?

      Yes

      No

6. As a child did you experience someone exposing their genitalia or breasts, view pornography, or witness sex of any type?

      Yes

      No

   a. Did it occur before age 10?

      Yes

      No

   b. Did it occur between the ages 10-20?

      Yes

      No

7. As an adult have you ever experienced someone inappropriately exposing their genitalia or breasts, forcing you to view pornography and/or witnessed sex of any type?

      Yes

      No

8. Have you ever experienced someone using God, religion, or their spiritual authority to control you, punish you or harm you in anyway?

      Yes

      No

   a. Did it occur before age 10?

      Yes

      No

   b. Did it occur between the ages 10-20?

      Yes

      No

   c. Did it occur after age 20?

      Yes

      No

9. Have you ever been forced/coerced to engage in bestiality?
   - Yes
   - No
   a. Did it occur before age 10?
      - Yes
      - No
   b. Did it occur between the ages 10-20?
      - Yes
      - No
   c. Did it occur after age 20?
      - Yes
      - No

10. Have you ever been forced/coerced to engage in any sexual behavior by anyone for their profit?
    - Yes
    - No
    a. Did it occur before age 10?
       - Yes
       - No
    b. Did it occur between the ages 10-20?
       - Yes
       - No
    c. Did it occur after age 20?
       - Yes
       - No
    d. Was it photographed or filmed?
       - Yes
       - No

11. Have you ever been locked up, caged in, barricaded in a room (basement, closet, shed, etc.) against your will?
    - Yes
    - No
    a. Did it occur before age 10?
       - Yes
       - No
    b. Did it occur between the ages 10-20?
       - Yes
       - No
    c. Did it occur after age 20?
       - Yes
       - No

12. Have you ever experienced being physically, emotionally, or spiritually neglected and/or abandoned by a parent, loved one or someone you were in close relationship?

        Yes

        No

    a. Did it occur before age 10?

        Yes

        No

    b. Did it occur between the ages 10-20?

        Yes

        No

    c. Did it occur after age 20?

        Yes

        No

13. Have you ever been part of a cult?

        Yes

        No

    a. Did it occur before age 10?

        Yes

        No

    b. Did it occur between the ages 10-20?

        Yes

        No

    c. Did it occur after age 20?

        Yes

        No

RECOVERY JOURNEY THUS FAR

1. Have you ever completed an inpatient detox/rehab program?

        Yes

        No

2. Have you ever completed an intensive outpatient or partial hospitalization?

        Yes

        No

3. Have you ever spent significant time with a counselor processing your past?

        Yes

        No

4. Have you ever worked through the 12 steps in a recovery group?

        Yes

        No

5. Have you ever worked through an in-depth inner healing program?

        Yes

        No

6. Have you forgiven your abusers or those who have hurt you?
   Yes
   No
7. Are you currently working toward forgiving your abusers or those who hurt you?
   Yes
   No
8. Are you frequently spiritually lifted up by your relationship with God?
   Yes
   No
9. Do you currently have a spiritual and/or recovery mentor or sponsor?
   Yes
   No
10. Do you currently have several safe accountability partners that you can be honest with (without being judged or criticized)?
    Yes
    No

*This tool is not meant to treat or diagnose anyone. It is only a tool to assess the possible impact previous events may have on your present and future.

Week 3

Fantasy Versus Reality

LISTENING GUIDE

Traumas and stressful events leave wounds in our spirit, soul, and body. Understanding just how deeply we've been wounded, will help us understand the realistic expectations for our recovery journey. The more deeply we've been wounded, the more complex and lengthier our recovery journey will be.

By understanding this, we can give ourselves more grace for the process. It is not a judgement on our value – we are priceless to God! Rather, it is to help us make the best strategy for a full recovery.

Factor #1: _____ emotional growth plate.

When trauma happens at a young age, it will affect your ability to grow emotionally healthy. It does not mean you cannot ever heal from the damage, but that it will take greater intervention and attention to heal the wound.

Factor #2: Type, severity, or length of _____.

Type – One sexual assault may have more severe damage than a physical or emotional trauma.

Severity – Witnessing a physical assault on another person would be less severe than experiencing the physical trauma yourself.

NOTES

Length – One kind of trauma repeatedly sustained over a long period of time may leave a greater wound than one severe traumatic event.

Multiple Traumas – If you have had several instances of trauma throughout your life, then the compounding of those wounds would likely make you more vulnerable and experience further trauma, especially if the trauma began in childhood.

Current Situation – If you are in a relationship or situation where you are still regularly experiencing abuse or trauma, this will significantly extend your recovery timeline, possibly even exponentially. We strongly recommend removing yourself from this person or situation as quickly as possible so that you can experience the full and complete healing God has for you.

Factor #3: _____ of investment and effort.

Like many programs, you will get more out of it if you are willing to invest effort and time into your recovery journey.

After shutting down or stuffing emotions for a long period of time, it can seem difficult to feel and examine the details of painful events or situations. However, this is the only way to experience full healing.

As with anything, too much is still too much. Over-feeling or getting ahead of the course and moving too fast will be as harmful as holding back – although there may be different consequences.

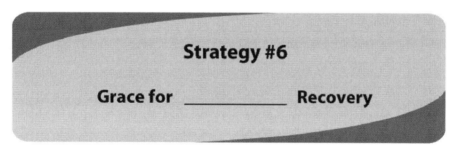

Strategy #6

Grace for _____ Recovery

This will be an up-and-down journey with some good days and bad days – sometimes good moments and bad moments in a short period of time.

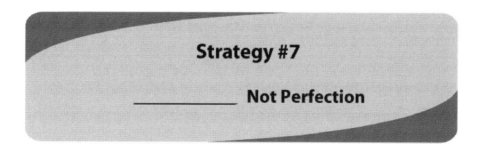

Strategy #7

_____ Not Perfection

NOTES

Instead of focusing on what is broken or not meeting your expectations, focus on recognizing the progress that has been made. If your tendency is to point out the imperfection, start intentionally changing your focus and point out the positive progress for yourself and others. Realistically, a recovery journey is about the baby steps moving forward toward healing.

Fantasy #1: _____ Fantasy

As long as you are striving to control others or your situation (in some cases, even ourselves) you are operating under a false belief that you have some kind of control. Striving to ensure an outcome will leave you frustrated and empty.

Whether or not we are consciously trying to control our lives or others, fear is often the motivating factor. God is the one who keeps us safe. We do not need to control our environment in order to be safe.

Remember, you are not God. It's not your job to get everything perfect or make sure others are performing the way you'd like. Let God be God and let go of the consequences.

Fantasy #2: _____ Fantasy

This is the false belief that life would better, we would be happier or more peaceful or successful, IF ONLY a condition were met.

This belief can be used to refuse to accept responsibility for your own actions and stay in a fantasy that you may find easier to accept.

It can also be used to avoid accepting a difficult reality and the emotions surrounding it by staying stuck in anger and accusation.

If you are an abuse victim, you may use this kind of thinking to attribute more of the responsibility to yourself rather than your abuser. For example, "If only I had been good, I wouldn't have needed to be punished."

Fantasy #3: _____ Fantasy

Unrealistic expectations of ourselves, others and God will disrupt our serenity every time they are not met.

Consequences of unmet expectations range anywhere from disappointment to intense grief. The higher you place your expectations and the more tightly you hold to those expectations then the more intense grieving process you can expect.

Often, expectations are not a conscious choice. But bringing awareness to expectations, intentionally setting the bar lower, and holding loosely the plans for the future are skills that can grow with practice.

NOTES

Fantasy #4: _____ Fantasy

This is the false belief that you are better than or stronger than God or others and that you can recover on your own without help.

God designed us to need His love and strength and wisdom. He designed us to need community in order to be healthy. Solitary confinement causes insanity and is used as torture for a reason.

It is not a sign of weakness to receive help. It is actually a sign of bravery, since it requires you to trust God and others.

WEEKLY WORSHIP
"We Believe" by Newsboys

DISCUSSION QUESTIONS

1. What do you feel has kept you from investing effort and time in your journey up to this point?

2. Do you find it hard to extend grace to yourself? Explain.

3. Which Fantasy did you feel you have most closely connected with--now or in the past?

What Healing/Recovery Looks Like for Me Worksheet
Week 3 Homework

Let's paint a picture of what life would be like without the brokenness, addiction, illness, victimization, or debilitating grief. This is the opportunity to start dreaming again. To build hope for a future that is brighter than today's mess. These questions are designed to help you think of new goals and dreams. A new you that you are choosing to become, one baby step at a time.

Note: This is not an exercise in fantasy. It is not about changing anyone else. It's not about manipulating the circumstances around us. It is not about denial. It is about beginning to see a new life ahead of us with God in the center.

Read the Serenity Prayer

God,
Grant me the serenity to accept the things I cannot change;
Courage to change the things I can;
and wisdom to know the difference.
Living one day at a time; enjoying one moment at a time;
Accepting hardships as the pathway to peace;
Taking, as Jesus did, this sinful world as it is, not as I would have it;
Trusting that You will make all things right if I surrender to Your Will;
So that I may be reasonably happy in this life
and supremely happy with You forever in the next.
Amen.

1. With the Serenity Prayer in mind, what would you like to change about your behaviors, patterns, or choices? Make a list. (Drugs or alcohol, fear, grief, codependency, victimization, bondage, etc. See questions 10-12 from Week 2 homework.)

2. In the question above, number each area in the order it is killing you or causing the most disruption in your life, one being the most severe. (For example, Ginny's story about dealing with alcohol before codependency, and Evonna addressing her physical health before being able to emotionally process.)

3. Fill out a "What Recovery/Healing Looks Like Form" for each area. Use extra paper if you need it for additional areas.

LIST

What Recovery/Healing Looks Like Form

Area of Change:	Number of Priority:
In this area of bondage/struggle, what would it look like to be free?	What would be different in your life if you successfully changed your choices in this area?
How would your schedule improve or look different if you healed or recovered in this area?	How would your finances improve or look different if you healed or recovered in this area?
How would your relationships improve or look different? (Not if you changed anyone else, but if YOU changed.)	What would it look like if you fully surrendered and totally trusted God instead of being destroyed by emotions and/or addictions in this area?
What kind of legacy would you leave behind at the end of your long life if you were healed, free, and whole in this area?	

What Recovery/Healing Looks Like Form

Area of Change:	Number of Priority:
In this area of bondage/struggle, what would it look like to be free?	What would be different in your life if you successfully changed your choices in this area?
How would your schedule improve or look different if you healed or recovered in this area?	How would your finances improve or look different if you healed or recovered in this area?
How would your relationships improve or look different? (Not if you changed anyone else, but if YOU changed.)	What would it look like if you fully surrendered and totally trusted God instead of being destroyed by emotions and/or addictions in this area?
What kind of legacy would you leave behind at the end of your long life if you were healed, free, and whole in this area?	

What Recovery/Healing Looks Like Form

Area of Change:	Number of Priority:
In this area of bondage/struggle, what would it look like to be free?	What would be different in your life if you successfully changed your choices in this area?
How would your schedule improve or look different if you healed or recovered in this area?	How would your finances improve or look different if you healed or recovered in this area?
How would your relationships improve or look different? (Not if you changed anyone else, but if YOU changed.)	What would it look like if you fully surrendered and totally trusted God instead of being destroyed by emotions and/or addictions in this area?
What kind of legacy would you leave behind at the end of your long life if you were healed, free, and whole in this area?	

What Recovery/Healing Looks Like Form

Area of Change:	Number of Priority:
In this area of bondage/struggle, what would it look like to be free?	What would be different in your life if you successfully changed your choices in this area?
How would your schedule improve or look different if you healed or recovered in this area?	How would your finances improve or look different if you healed or recovered in this area?
How would your relationships improve or look different? (Not if you changed anyone else, but if YOU changed.)	What would it look like if you fully surrendered and totally trusted God instead of being destroyed by emotions and/or addictions in this area?
What kind of legacy would you leave behind at the end of your long life if you were healed, free, and whole in this area?	

What Recovery/Healing Looks Like Form

Area of Change:	Number of Priority:
In this area of bondage/struggle, what would it look like to be free?	What would be different in your life if you successfully changed your choices in this area?
How would your schedule improve or look different if you healed or recovered in this area?	How would your finances improve or look different if you healed or recovered in this area?
How would your relationships improve or look different? (Not if you changed anyone else, but if YOU changed.)	What would it look like if you fully surrendered and totally trusted God instead of being destroyed by emotions and/or addictions in this area?
What kind of legacy would you leave behind at the end of your long life if you were healed, free, and whole in this area?	

What Recovery/Healing Looks Like Form

Area of Change:	Number of Priority:
In this area of bondage/struggle, what would it look like to be free?	What would be different in your life if you successfully changed your choices in this area?
How would your schedule improve or look different if you healed or recovered in this area?	How would your finances improve or look different if you healed or recovered in this area?
How would your relationships improve or look different? (Not if you changed anyone else, but if YOU changed.)	What would it look like if you fully surrendered and totally trusted God instead of being destroyed by emotions and/or addictions in this area?

What kind of legacy would you leave behind at the end of your long life if you were healed, free, and whole in this area?

Week 4

Who God Is

LISTENING GUIDE

Part #1: _____ Being

God is a trinity – He is three in one. This is a mystery to our finite minds.

Since we were made in God's image, we are made of three components just as God is made of three components.

Your Spirit is the reflection of the "GOD the Father" part of the trinity.

Your Soul is your mind, will, and emotions and is the reflection of the Comforter (Holy Spirit) part of the trinity.

Your Body is the physical, tangible part of you. It is the reflection of Jesus within the trinity.

Although all three of our parts are connected, they are not always in line with each other. For example, you can receive healing in your soul or spirit, but you may still have illness in your body.

Part #2: _____ Nature

NOTES

God has a personality and a way of being! Here are some examples:

Consistency – He is the same every day. He is always present; He never leaves. He honors all of His promises and doesn't waver or change His mind.

Loving – The love and compassion that He has for you is greater than anything you have experienced on a human level and it is never ending.

Creative – God creates beauty and healing, renewal and restoration. He creates opportunities and makes His mercies new every morning!

Just – God, being sovereign, established the rules of the physical universe and the Kingdom of Heaven in the spiritual realm. He remains true to those rules and the promises He made to His children. God does not make sure everyone receives fair (i.e. equal) treatment, but He does remain just. His rules and promises still allow for His generosity and vengeance and discipline to be distributed as He sees fit in this life and in heaven.

Giving – The Lord gave His only Son to die on the cross and be separated from Him so that you and I would never be separated from God. His mercy and grace and love are endless.

Part #3: Intentional _____

His design is for this world and your place and calling within it are complete from beginning to end. He is not bound by time.

He wants to redeem every piece of brokenness in your story, no matter how large or small you think it is.

Even if He hasn't redeemed parts of your story yet, you can be sure that if you walk in obedience to God one step at a time, He has a plan to use it for His Kingdom.

You cannot mess up God's plan because He has always known the choices you'd make.

You can rest in the perfection of His plan.

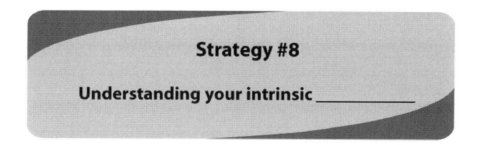

Strategy #8

Understanding your intrinsic _____

NOTES

His design includes your priceless value! Nothing you do will increase or decrease your value in God's eyes. You are created in His flawless image.

God pre-packaged you and assigned your value!

Since God is sovereign, He is the only source of your value. No decision, event, or opinion held by you or anyone else can change that your value has already been assigned by God.

WEEKLY WORSHIP
"Who You Say I Am" by Hillsong

DISCUSSION QUESTIONS
1. What part of God's nature have you personally experienced?

2. What part of God's nature have you not experienced that you would like too?

3. Since we were made in God's image, how does understanding God's nature help you see yourself differently?

Who God Made You to Be Worksheet
Week 4 Homework

God created us in His image. This means we need to know who God is to understand who we were created to be. These questions are designed to help you develop a deeper understanding of who you are, and who you are not, based on Truth.

1. What do you know about God's nature?

2. How does knowing about God's nature help you recognize your shortcomings?

3. What does God say about you in His word?

4. What would your life look like if you saw yourself through God's eyes and not through your own eyes or the world's eyes?

5. Review the "Who We Are" worksheet that lists scriptures. Are there truths on the list that you struggle to believe about yourself? What would it look like for you if you could believe that truth?

6. What lies are you believing about yourself? Find a scripture verse that speaks truth to that area and speak it over yourself daily.

Who I Am Scriptures
Week 4 Homework

This list of "I am" statements are derived from specific scripture references. Read through the list of "I am" statements out loud. If any of them are confusing or difficult to accept, write the scripture out and ask God to help you embrace this truth completely. If you find a new concept to be promising or intriguing, spend more time exploring the concept and enjoy embracing it at a new level.

I am his friend. (John 15:15)

I am chosen. (John 15:16)

I am complete in Him. (Colossians 2:10)

I am fearfully and wonderfully made. (Psalm 139:14)

I am a new creation. (2 Corinthians 5:17)

I am His workmanship. (Ephesians 2:10)

I am a child of the light. (1 Thessalonians 5:5)

I am a child of the most high! (John 1:12, 1 John 4:4)

I am an heir of God and a joint heir with Christ. (Romans 8:17)

I am more than a conqueror. (Romans 8:37)

I am adopted as God's sons and daughters through Jesus Christ. (Ephesians 1:5)

My body is the temple of the Holy Spirit. (1 Corinthians 6:19)

I am the head and not the tail, I am at the top and never the bottom. (Deuteronomy 28:13)

I am holy. (Ephesians 1:4)

I am a member of the royal priesthood. (1 Peter 2:9)

I am set apart. (Psalm 4:3)

I am totally and completely forgiven. (1 John 1:9)

I am God's intentional and perfectly planned creation. (Psalm 139:13)

Who God Is Scriptures
Week 4 Homework

Read through the list of descriptors about God. If any of them are confusing or difficult to accept, write the scripture out and ask God to help you embrace this truth completely. If you find a new concept to be promising or intriguing, spend more time exploring the concept and enjoy embracing it at a new level.

God is:

Accepting - Romans 15:7
Available - Jeremiah 29:13
Caring - 1 Peter 5:7
Close - Psalm 34:18-19
Comforter - 2 Corinthians 1:3-4
Compassionate - Lamentations 3:22-23
Deliverer - Psalm 18:2
Encouraging - Romans 15:4
Faithful - 1 Thessalonians 5:24
Father - Galatians 4:6
Forgiving - Daniel 9:9
Generous - James 1:17
Giving - John 3:16
Good - Psalm 106:1
Gracious - Ephesians 2:8-9
Healer - Psalm 103:3
Humble - Matthew 11:28-30
Light - Ephesians 5:8
Lord - Acts 10:36
Love - 1 John 4:16
Loyal - Deuteronomy 31:6
Merciful - Psalm 86:15
Mighty - Psalm 24:8
Miracle-worker - Hebrews 2:4

Omnipresent - Psalm 139:7-10
Omniscient - Psalm 139:16
Patient - 2 Peter 3:15
Powerful - Joshua 4:24
Redeemer - Isaiah 34:5
Refreshing - Acts 3:19-20
Refuge - Psalm 46:1, Psalm 91
Restorer - Psalm 23:3
Reviver - Psalm 19:7
Righteous - Psalm 89:14
Rock - Deuteronomy 32:4
Servant - Mark 10:45
Shepherd - Psalm 23:1
Shield - Proverbs 30:5
Sovereign - Daniel 5:21b
Sympathetic - Hebrews 4:15-16
Teacher - Isaiah 28:26
Transformer - 2 Corinthians 5:17
Trustworthy - Deuteronomy 7:9
Truth - John 14:6
Unchangeable - Malachi 3:6
Understanding - Isaiah 40:28
Warrior - Exodus 14:14
Wise - Job 12:13

Week 5

God's Heart for Restoration

LISTENING GUIDE

Truth #1: God _____ us.

Even before sin entered the world, Jesus was scheduled to be the sacrifice that would give everyone the chance to be redeemed.

Jesus died on the cross to pay for your sins and shortcomings, so you would not have to pay for your sins.

You can repent (stop, turn around, go the other way) and claim that redemption. You can turn to Him at any point. You do not need to be "fixed" before you claim your redemption.

Redemption is more than a one-time decision. It is a lifestyle and posture of the heart.

Truth #2: God wants to _____.

God's plan for restoration was built into the foundation of the world and inside His plan for the world.

God's grace for restoration is extended toward those who repent because He loves us so completely.

NOTES

Restoration is more than just salvation. There is also restoration of your heart and relationships and renewal of the mind.

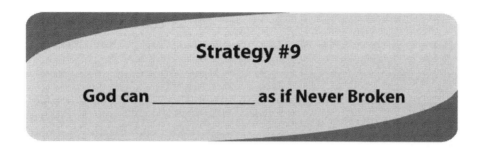

This kind of healing is for YOU as well! With God, this is absolutely possible! Nothing is impossible for God!

Each day, we have to choose to believe that we are receiving redemption and restoration from God along the journey.

Truth #3: _____ healing is available.

Healing miracles were not just in Biblical times, they are for today as well! God's heart for healing has not changed.

A creative God can recreate what's been damaged. His generous heart wants to heal you and He will when it is for your eternal good. God is the only one who can determine who and when and how the miracle will be for their good.

Disciples were given the authority to do even greater works – disciples like you!

WEEKLY WORSHIP
"Mended" by Matthew West

DISCUSSION QUESTIONS

1. Can you share one area in your life that has been damaged and/or broken that you desire healing in?

2. Strategy #9 (God Can Restore as if Never Broken) can be a hard concept to understand in healing. What would it look like for you if God restored your life as if never broken?

3. Has God ever healed you in any way? If so, does that give you hope for more healing?

What's Broken Needs Healing Worksheet
Week 5 Homework

The following questions will help you identify the areas in your life that are broken and need healing. As you work through these questions, make sure you are giving yourself grace. We don't want the enemy to use this as an opportunity to accuse you, add shame, or blame you. Be kind to yourself as you do this assignment.

1. List the areas in your life that you feel are damaged and/or broken.

2. Did the Life Events Assessment bring up any old memories or new areas of brokenness or struggle that you were not yet aware of?

3. We have said "Hey, you eat an elephant one bite at a time." What area in your life consumes most of your energy (physical, emotional spiritual)?

4. Number those areas of brokenness from question #3, with 1 being the biggest area that consumes your thoughts, time, etc.

5. Do you feel that your current areas of struggle are keeping you from living a life of fullness in God? How?

6. Which of the areas in questions 1-3 are you ready to surrender to God?

7. When you are ready to surrender, read the following prayer out loud for each area:

God, I recognize that I have been damaged/broken in the area of _____ (fill in the blank with areas you listed). I recognize that I cannot handle this on my own. I surrender it to You. I place it at the foot of the cross and ask You to come into this area and bring the healing only You can provide. Please renew my mind and guide my steps now and as I move forward. Help me to continue to surrender this every day, one day at a time. In Jesus' name, Amen.

Physical Health Family Tree Exercise
Week 5 Homework

In this exercise you will draw a diagram of your family tree and the physical conditions, illnesses, and/or addictions. This will help you to identify family patterns to understand where you come from and/or where your family is headed. To give you enough room, there is a full page provided for each of your parents' families.

There is also a sample family tree provided on the following page to give you some inspiration. You do not need to include boxes for any category of family member that are not in your family. (For example, you do not need a box for cousins, if you do not have any cousins.)

If you have children and grandchildren, you may include them on either family tree. You are not required to write them twice, but you may wish to do so if you want to see the correlation to each parent's family.

Physical Health Family Tree (Sample)
Mother's Side

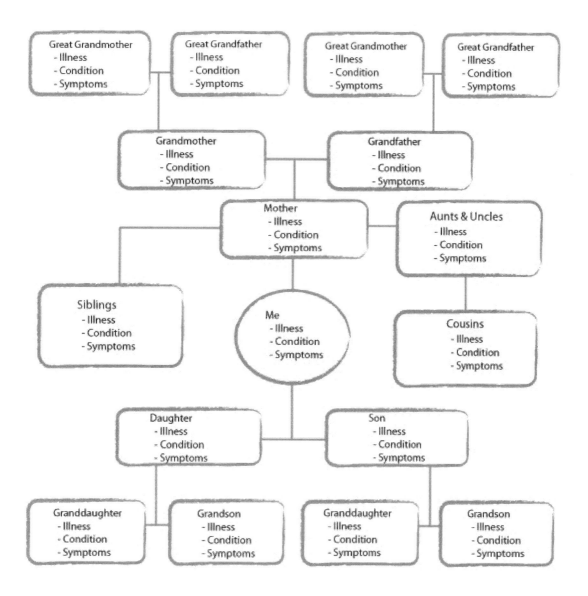

Physical Health Family Tree
Mother's Side

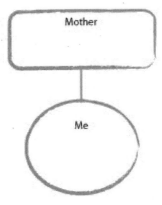

Physical Health Family Tree
Father's Side

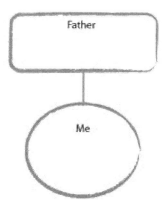

Week 6

The Love of Father God

LISTENING GUIDE

Our earthly fathers are all human, therefore they have all fallen short in some way. For some of us, our fathers were abusive and left a deep, painful wound. For others of us, our fathers were relatively healthy, but by falling short of perfection, they still left a wound.

Understanding that separating the wounds our earthly fathers left from God's perfect love is important to our healing journey because…

Reason #1: _____ your view of God.

Our earthly father's behavior shapes and molds our understanding of all fathers. Because of that, we instinctually assign the hurts of our earthly fathers to Father God.

If we believe our earthly fathers are similar to Father God, our relationship with God will be under false pretenses.

It's important to study and understand the character traits of Father God in order to know what kind of father we are trusting and what kind of role He will play in our lives.

Reason #2: Creates _____.

NOTES

God is love. The essence of His being is relationship. When there are wounds from our child-hood, especially from those in human father roles, our capacity to receive His love and be in healthy relationship with Him is damaged.

If we cannot fully receive His love, then we are left with an emptiness inside that we will seek to fill with someone or something else.

Since God is the source of all love we will not be capable of loving others out of the overflow of His love. Instead, we will try to manufacture love or attempt to control or manipulate others into showing us love and connection. The problem is human love will never satisfy or fill the wound our father created.

Reason #3: The father wound _____ your spirit, soul, and body.

This is not the only wound that damages us on all three levels. However, the father wound has a particularly powerful impact on all three levels because it mirrors our relationship with Father God.

Any time our relationship with Father God is blocked, warped, or damaged, we will be impact-ed on all three levels of our being.

Comparison #1: God's _____ love versus human love.

God's love is unconditional, unlike human love, which has a limited capacity.

God is willing to do whatever is necessary for our eternal best because His needs are met with-in the trinity, where human fathers have human needs that limit their emotional and physical ability to sacrifice.

Comparison #2: God's _____ versus flawed discipline.

God's justice comes from a place of love and redemption, where sometimes human discipline comes from a place of anger, frustration, or a need to control.

God's discipline is for our growth and education and eternal good.

Read Psalm 23. The rod is used to beat off the enemies who might hurt the sheep. The staff is used to keep the sheep from running away or falling off a cliff. Safety is found in the discipline of the shepherd.

Comparison #3: God's consistent _____ versus human absence.

God's ability to be ever present and meet us exactly where we are is not impeded by the physi-cal restrictions that human fathers operate under.

NOTES

God's ability to provide and nurture is not restricted by past hurts, limited emotional bandwidth, immaturity, or lack of resources.

Comparison #4: God's _____ versus human abandonment.

No matter who we are, what we've done, or what's been done to us, we have the opportunity to be adopted by God when we accept Jesus as our personal Lord and Savior.

We never have to be without a father or family that has committed to love us and provide for us eternally.

There are benefits to understanding God's character and how He interacts with you as His child.

Benefit #1: _____ Order

God provides a protective covering for His children.

God provides order out of the chaos that the enemy wants to throw our way.

God is very specific about family order and the role of husbands and wives, parents, and children. This is not an order of importance. This is not the order of power. This is a healthy guide to help families follow God and function in a healthy and supportive manner for everyone in them. The guidelines are there to protect against lies and chaos that families can be vulnerable to when Godly order is ignored.

Benefit #2: _____

When we run to God and foster a deeper relationship with Him, we receive healing in our spirit, soul, and body. The healing creates opportunity for us to receive and then give more love and grace and mercy. As a result, we experience greater unity with God, ourselves, and others around us.

Benefit #3: _____ in your spirit, soul, and body.

God provides supernatural healing through love and relationship with Him.

Human fathers and mothers can only be examples of this love. Their best efforts can only reflect a piece of the enormity of love that God has for us. They were never meant to be the replacement for a relationship with God.

Hurt people hurt people. And since we live in a broken world, fighting "not against flesh and blood," we cannot help but live in the world and be hurt by hurting people.

NOTES

We have the choice to stay stuck in the hurt and blame-game or the choice to run to God and offer forgiveness to others for the wounds we received.

If you have inflicted any wounds, intentionally or unintentionally, you have the choice to ignore the past or accept forgiveness from God and stop living with denial, shame, or guilt.

WEEKLY WORSHIP
"Fierce" by Jesus Culture

DISCUSSION QUESTIONS
1. What behaviors of your biological father shaped or distorted your view of God?

2. What characteristics of God as a Loving Father are the most needed in your life?

3. How badly did your biological father distort your view of God as a father?

Loving Father Description Worksheet
Week 6 Homework

It can be difficult to know what a loving father looks like if we've never had one. In this exercise, we are going to guide you through a process to help you have a better picture of who a loving father should be. This way, you will be better able to start seeing God as your "Loving Heavenly Father" who wants to love and bless you.

Read the following attributes of God as a Loving Father. This is not an exhaustive list, but rather the start of one. Are these characteristics that you associate with a "father figure"? Maybe not, but they are still true of God as your "Heavenly Father."

Description of God as a Loving Heavenly Father

Loving	Provider	Merciful
Available	Defender	Strong
Sacrificial	Preparer	Constant
Kind	Trainer	Patient
Honest	Goes Ahead	Present
Intentional	Joyous	Caring
Surprising	Open	
Direct	Proud of His Children	
Fights for His Children	Generous	

1. Have you seen God as your Loving Father before? Why or why not?

2. What additional characteristics have you thought of that would help you relate to God as a Loving Father who is meeting your specific needs as His child?

3. Choose your 5 favorite characteristics and write a sentence for each with "God is a Loving Father to me because He _____ (finish the sentence)."

4. Read the chart on the next page that describes how God may handle our behaviors. Are any of the responses on the chart a surprise to you?

5. Have you experienced any responses from God that are described in the chart on the next page? If so, which ones? Describe what that experience was like for you.

NOTES

When I am…	God will often…
Demanding or asking for an explanation	• Listen. • Show kindness, even in silence. • Provide explanation in ways that we can understand without overloading or hurting us. • Provide supernatural revelation in His perfect timing. • Pour out His love.
Demanding God to bring what we desire in the time we desire it	• Offer silence to give us time to understand why He did not do it our way. • Give us conviction to follow His will that will be for our eternal benefit, not just put out today's fire. • Provide guidance about the next step we are to take for His perfect will to be accomplished. • Pour out His love.
Angry and/or frustrated at God	• Remain calm and not be threatened. • Stay present throughout. • Respond with scripture or Biblical truth. • Pour out His love.
Feeling depressed	• Stay present, even in silence. • Provide encouragement through people, books, television, sermons, nature, etc. • Pour out His love.
Complaining or whining about my situation	• Listen patiently. • Gently point out to me where my perspective is incorrect. • Remind me to worship Him. • Remind me to focus on gratitude. • Pour out His love.
Being disobedient to God	• Convict my heart of wrongdoing, but never shame me. • Provide me with a warning. • Allow the consequences of my disobedience to catch up with me so that I will learn from my poor decision. • Pour out His love.
Asking for help	• Provide wisdom. • Provide peace when I surrender to His will. • Provide understanding. • Provide guidance. • Pour out His love.

The Love of The Father Scriptures
Week 6 Homework

Look up the following scriptures and write them out in the spaces provided.
These scriptures describe God's character as our Father and/or our relationship with Him. If any of them are confusing or difficult to accept, study the scripture in context and ask God to help you embrace this truth completely. If you find a new concept to be promising or intriguing, spend more time exploring the concept and enjoy embracing it at a new level.

Psalm 68:5-6 _____

_____

_____

Matthew 6:8 _____

_____

_____

Matthew 6:26 _____

_____

_____

Matthew 7:11 _____

_____

_____

Matthew 18:14 _____

_____

_____

John 14:16 _____

_____

_____

Romans 8:15 _____

_____

_____

Romans 12:38,39 _____

_____

_____

Ephesians 1:3-5 _____

_____

_____

1 John 3:1 _____

_____

_____

Additional Scriptures

Here are some additional scriptures for you to look up if you wish to continue exploring God as a Loving Father.

- Deuteronomy 32:10
- Isaiah 64:8
- Matthew 6:6
- Luke 15:20b, 22-24
- John 14:1-3
- John 15:16
- 2 Corinthians 6:18
- Ephesians 2:19
- Ephesians 3:16-19
- Ephesians 3:6

Father's Repentance and Blessing Exercise
Week 6 Homework

Wounds from biological fathers (progenitor) can be hugely impacting, so we want to stop the damage and start the healing. We suggest you get a safe man who is a "father" type figure in your life to speak this over you. If one is not available, please read this as you listen to the audio recording we've provided. We know from personal experience how difficult and uncomfortable this process can be. Please do this exercise despite the negative emotions it may trigger. It will be powerful in your healing process.

Note: This may take multiple times to reach the deepest places of damage in this area. Come back to this as many times as you need to during your healing journey. *

Download audio version: https://bloominthedark.org/rs4l/fathers-repentance-and-blessing

Father's Repentance and Blessing:

As the representative of a biological father who wasn't available,
Didn't know how to express love, abandoned you, abused you, didn't protect you,
Rejected you, just wasn't able to be who you needed him to be, or died,
I want to say I'm sorry.

I'm sorry for not fulfilling my role as a loving father.
I'm sorry for not providing for you, protecting you, or taking care of your heart.
I'm sorry for abandoning you, hurting you, abusing you, or neglecting you.
I'm sorry for not loving you, not showing love to you, or not saying "I love you."
I'm sorry for every way I let you down, wasn't there for you, dismissed or rejected you.
I'm sorry for everything that I put above your wellbeing.

I repent to God for myself and my generations before me.
I repent for my brokenness, my lack of parenting, my weaknesses, and failures.
I repent for every way I followed the enemy and his lies.
I repent for every sin that brought damage or curses on you.
I ask for and accept God's forgiveness.

I want to tell you, "I LOVE YOU!"
You are cherished, loved, lovable, and deserving of love.
I am grateful to God for creating you.
You are fearfully and wonderfully made.
You were made perfectly by God's design.
I am blessed to be your father.

I want to bless you with all of God's richest blessings.
May God bless you and guard you.
May the light of God shine upon you, and may God be gracious to you.
May the presence of God be with you and give you peace.
May you become the parent you desire to become.
May you and your children be strong and healthy.
May the Almighty help you.

May He bless you with blessings from heaven above and the earth beneath.
May the Lord nurture you, feed you, and provide for you abundantly.
May your Heavenly Father teach you, guide you, and give you His wisdom.
May the grace, mercy and peace of our Lord rest on you.
May you trust in the Lord and always run to Him first with every need.
May you be above and not beneath, the head and not the tail.
May you have dominion over everything that is contrary to God.
Cursed be everyone who curses you, and blessed be everyone who blesses you.
May your calling be established, your path be made straight, and your mission successful.
And may you love the Lord with all your soul, mind, and strength and serve Him only.
Be blessed.

Scriptures used to create this prayer:
Genesis 27:28-29
Genesis 27:39-40
Genesis 48:4
Genesis 49:24-25
Psalm 78:5–7
Psalm 139:14
1 Timothy 1:2

* For the Mother's Repentance and Blessings and Spiritual Leader's Repentance and Blessings, see the appendices.

Week 7

Surrender to God

LISTENING GUIDE

Step #1: _____ to let Him.

Choose to let God have control over your life.

Full surrender to God is a choice we have to make every day, sometimes a thousand times per day. It is not a one-time decision. Each time our emotions rise and we are tempted to take matters into our own hands without consulting or following God, we have to choose to give Him the reigns.

When we feel ourselves striving or becoming frustrated or discontented with God, others, or our circumstances, it's time to bring that frustration to God and surrender it. No circumstance is too large or too small to surrender to God.

Step #2: Not _____ on your own ideas.

Recognizing that our own ideas have caused us pain and frustration, helps us turn away from them and allows God to have sovereignty in our lives instead.

Many times God gives us guidance through sponsors and mentors who have walked the journey ahead of us and experienced both the brokenness we are familiar with and the healing we are looking for.

NOTES

We can experience more peace by accepting that our ideas are limited to our finite understanding. We can trust that a God who sees the beginning and end of our journeys will be able to better guide our path for our most complete healing.

Step #3: _____ the things you cannot change.

The Serenity Prayer: "God, grant me the serenity to accept the things I cannot change, courage to change the things I can, and wisdom to know the difference. Living one day at a time, enjoying one moment at a time. Accepting hardship as the pathway to peace. Taking, as Jesus did, this sinful world as it is, not as I would have it. Trusting that you will make all things right if I surrender to your will, so that I will be reasonably happy in this life and supremely happy in the next. Amen." (Reinhold Neibuhr)

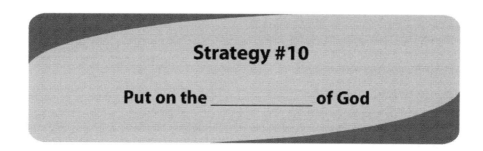

Strategy #10

Put on the _____ of God

As it says in Ephesians 6:12, we struggle not against flesh and blood. Therefore, God has given us His armor to fight against our enemies in the spirit realm.

Belt of Truth

The belt on a soldier's uniform was meant to help them stand straight and tall in order to carry the rest of the armor. It also protects the core of the soldier.

We are to keep the truth of God's promises close to our core, specifically the truth of who God says we are and what He promises us.

Breastplate of Righteousness

The breastplate on a soldier's uniform covers the chest, shoulders, and stomach. It is the area with the most vital organs, like our heart and lungs.

When our heart is surrendered and in line with God's, then we can walk in righteousness (a.k.a. right standing) with God.

When we wear the breastplate of righteousness, we can keep an open, vulnerable heart toward God, and He will keep it safe from enemy attack damaging such a vital part of us.

NOTES

Feet Shod with the Preparation of the Gospel of Peace

A warrior's feet need a firm grip to stand and fight on all kinds of terrain and soil.

When we have the gospel of peace as the solid foundation of our faith, then we can stand as if we are on God's solid rock no matter what terrain a vulnerable situation may present. This helps us not only to stand, but also to advance against the enemy.

According to Colossians 1:20-21, Jesus created peace between us and God when He died on the cross. Therefore, those shoes give us direct access to God.

Shield of Faith

This shield blocks the flaming arrows of the enemy. These can be tangible attacks such as illness, loss, physical attack, etc., or intangible attacks such as temptations to lash out, manipulate, fall into self-pity, take offense, or withhold forgiveness.

When we see the flaming arrows or feel their heat, we do not have to be harmed by them. We can raise our shield of faith and stop them from having any harmful effects on our spirit, soul, or body.

Helmet of Salvation

Belief in Jesus Christ as our savior guards our mind.

When the Holy Spirit comes in, He can and will remind us of truth and scripture we need to keep our eyes and mind on Jesus and His saving power.

Sword of the Spirit, which is the Word of God

The Word of God is living and powerful. It is useful for instruction and training.

The Word of God cuts through the lies of the enemy and leaves them defenseless and without the power to touch us, let alone harm us.

Prayer

These pieces of armor are essential for fighting in the spirit. However, prayer is the key piece that attaches the armor to us and keeps the armor in position as we fight.

Prayer is foundational to the armor. Without prayer, we will be naked and unprotected.

NOTES

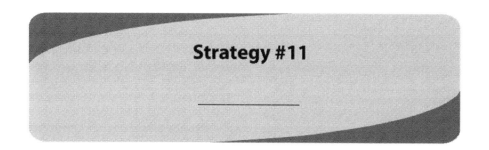

Strategy #11

_____

Romans 12:1-2 (NIV) "Therefore I urge you brothers and sisters, in view of God's mercy, to offer your bodies as a living sacrifice, holy and pleasing to God – this is your true and proper worship. Do not conform to the pattern of this world but be transformed by the renewing of your mind. Then you will be able to test and approve what God's will is – His good, pleasing, and perfect will."

Worship is:
- Worship is a posture of the heart to be surrendered to our loving and mighty God.
- Worship is an action. Sometimes that looks like shouting or singing praise to God. Other times, it looks like sacrificing comfort or something we want in order to follow God and His will.
- Out of surrender comes a desire to be obedient and walk in God's will.

Worship is not:
- Worship is not limited to simply singing.
- When our heart is not surrendered to God and we are praising or sacrificing out of a desire to earn God's approval or convince Him to give us what we want, then that is not worship. That is religion based on an exchange rather than a relationship rooted in boundless grace and unconditional love.

WEEKLY WORSHIP
"I Surrender" by Hillsong

DISCUSSION QUESTIONS
1. What areas of your life are you ready and willing to surrender?

2. What has or is keeping you from choosing to let Him have control?

3. What is the first thing that would change if you truly surrendered to God and let Him have control?

Armor of God Scripture Exercise
Week 7 Homework

Read the following scripture and listen to the audio version every day this week, or whenever you need it.

Download the audio version at: https://bloominthedark.org/rs4l/armor-of-god

Ephesians 6:10-18 (NKJV)

"Finally, my brethren, be strong in the Lord and in the power of His might. Put on the whole armor of God, that you may be able to stand against the wiles of the devil. For we do not wrestle against flesh and blood, but against principalities, against powers, against the rulers of the darkness of this age, against spiritual hosts of wickedness in the heavenly places. Therefore take up the whole armor of God, that you may be able to withstand in the evil day, and having done all, to stand.

Stand therefore, having girded your waist with truth, having put on the breastplate of righteousness, and having shod your feet with the preparation of the gospel of peace; above all, taking the shield of faith with which you will be able to quench all the fiery darts of the wicked one. And take the helmet of salvation, and the sword of the Spirit, which is the word of God; praying always with all prayer and supplication in the Spirit, being watchful to this end with all perseverance and supplication for all the saints."

Create Worship Playlist Worksheet
Week 7 Homework

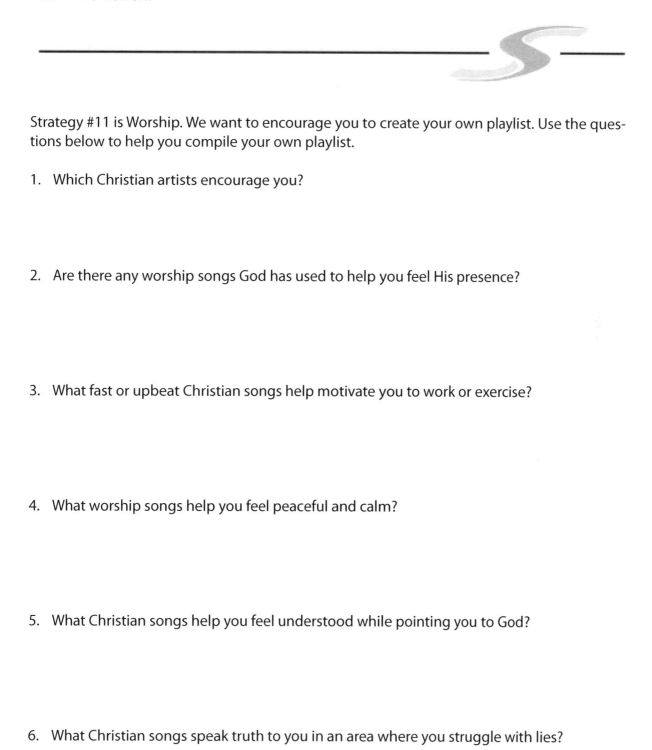

Strategy #11 is Worship. We want to encourage you to create your own playlist. Use the questions below to help you compile your own playlist.

1. Which Christian artists encourage you?

2. Are there any worship songs God has used to help you feel His presence?

3. What fast or upbeat Christian songs help motivate you to work or exercise?

4. What worship songs help you feel peaceful and calm?

5. What Christian songs help you feel understood while pointing you to God?

6. What Christian songs speak truth to you in an area where you struggle with lies?

NOTES

Worship Playlist
Week 7 Homework

Lesson Name	Song	Artist
What to Expect	"Freedom Hymn"	Austin French
Saying Hello to Reality	"No Longer Slave"	Bethel
Fantasy vs Reality	"We Believe"	Newsboys
Who God Is	"Who You Say I Am"	Hillsong
God's Heart for Restoration	"Mended"	Matthew West
The Love of Father God	"Fierce"	Jesus Culture
Surrender to God	"I Surrender"	Hillsong
Positive Coping Tools	"Tremble - Live"	Mosaic MSC
Progression of Sin	"God I Look To You"	Bethel
Cognitive Distortions	"You Say"	Lauren Daigle
You Are NOT Your Emotions	"God Help Me"	Plumb

This list is also available in the appendices.

Week 8

Positive Coping Tools

LISTENING GUIDE

You can start to use these strategies and coping immediately!

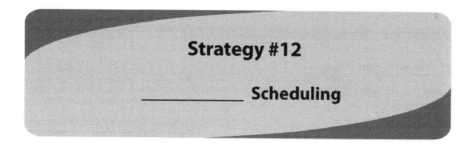

Strategy #12

_____ **Scheduling**

Emotional scheduling is the process of scheduling activities around the emotional processing needs for each moment.

If you have a counseling appointment in the early afternoon, be sure to schedule recovery time afterward, rather than schedule a meeting or activity where you'll need full adult processing (strategizing, multitasking, complex thinking, etc.)

If you know you'll be having a difficult meeting or task, you may want to schedule extra time beforehand to worship, ground, or pray with a friend to prepare.

NOTES

If possible, schedule a healthy physical release – going for a walk, dancing in your office, art class or sketch time.

Employ Strategy #1 (Be Honest With Yourself) and Strategy #6 (Grace for Realistic Recovery) when making your daily or weekly schedule. Then, as you walk through your week, make note and adjust where you may need more or less time to recover or prepare for activities. This is a learning process and you should expect to make adjustments. Remember Strategy #7 (Progress Not Perfection).

Whenever possible, be aware of your available bandwidth to focus. You may not have the ability to take time alone that you need, but you may be able to choose your next task or activity based on your available emotional bandwidth.

For small emotional bandwidth, working with your hands to clean or fold laundry might be an option. In an office, simple data entry or filing is a way to continue moving forward until you have recovered enough to gain back the bandwidth for more high functioning tasks.

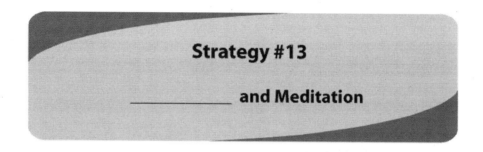

Strategy #13

_____ **and Meditation**

Schedule prayer and meditation during a quiet block of time as often as possible – daily or several days per week. You'll want to protect this time, as distractions are likely.

In addition to prayer and meditation (listening time), suggestions for this time include any combination of the following that feed your soul:
- o Worship music
- o Reading the Bible
- o Journaling
- o Reading a devotional
- o *Bloom Forward Journal*

This is not meant to be a legalistic practice. If not being able to follow the schedule is causing you to shame yourself, take a step back. Speak with your sponsor or mentor to discover what part of the current plan doesn't work for you. Come up with a different plan or schedule that will feed rather than drain you.

The Bible tells us to pray without ceasing. We can reach out to Him in prayer and meditation over the course of the day. Prayer does not have to be relegated to one part of our day.

NOTES

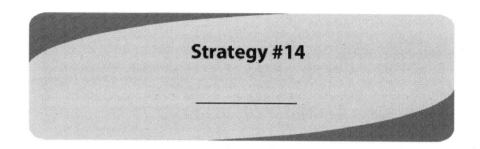

Strategy #14

_____

Gratitude helps us to see the blessings we've already received from God rather than focus on the pain or hardship or lack. We can stop comparing our lives with others' and start celebrating the gifts we have been given.

Making daily gratitude lists is a great way to train our minds over time and create more neural pathways in the brain to look for the gratitude as a reflex rather than a last resort.

Every day, in every moment, there is always something to be grateful for – even in the midst of deep pain and brokenness. If you are having trouble finding it, ask the Holy Spirit to reveal to you all that you can be grateful for.

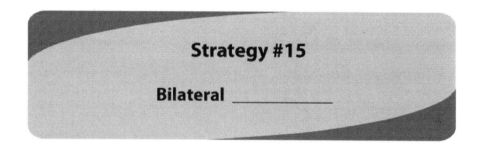

Strategy #15

Bilateral _____

This is where we are engaging both sides of the brain as we process events, concepts, or emotions. It helps to make connections between the feeling and concrete thinking parts for your brain. (Fun fact: This is why so many of us get our best ideas in the shower!)

The most common way to do this would be to engage in physical activity that uses both sides of your body while discussing, praying, or thinking about a difficult or painful topic.

Suggestions include:
- Exercising: walking, dancing, kayaking
- Creating a piece of art
- Arts and Crafts
- Washing the car
- Yard work, gardening

This helps you to make connections, understand, and come to accept the reality of what you are processing much more quickly than if you were remaining still.

NOTES

This also helps to release physical tension that can build up as a result of our intense emotions.

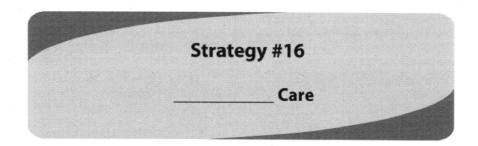

Strategy #16

_____ Care

Areas of basic self care practices are personal hygiene, eating balanced meals, getting enough sleep, and making personal connections.

How well we practice basic self care is an indicator of our overall emotional health. When we are stable or thriving on a soul-level, we can easily perform basic self care in these areas. (Please note: There are some exceptions. Certain physical conditions can prevent consistent, healthy sleep patterns or certain activities.)

We can go through seasons where our emotional processing can take up so much bandwidth, that we ignore areas of our basic self care. Also, hormones or feelings of depression can make basic self care seem impossible.

For some, ignoring self care comes from a place of feeling unworthy or intentionally acting to inflict personal harm.

If this is a season where one or more areas of basic self care have not been attainable, we recommend you contact a professional counselor and tell your support system the reality of your struggles. It is so important NOT to isolate, especially if reaching out is the last thing you want to do.

Higher level self care includes the previous strategies in this lesson (Prayer and Meditation, Emotional Scheduling, Bilateral Processing, Gratitude) and ALL of the strategies in this course.

WEEKLY WORSHIP
"Tremble – Live" by Mosaic MSC

NOTES

DISCUSSION QUESTIONS

1. In what areas of your life have you neglected self care?

2. What are some activities, hobbies, etc. that fill your cup? What would it look like for you to include 2 of those in your schedule this next week?

3. Do you need help putting together your self care plan? Who might help you with that?

Comprehensive Action Plan Worksheet
Week 8 Homework

Many of us have times when we're struggling and not able to make the best decisions. To help us with that, we're going to build a healthy/safe "Comprehensive Action Plan" that you can implement no matter how small, young, weak, stupid, or clueless you *feel* in that moment.

1. Who are your top safe people who can help you when you're triggered or struggling? Make a list with contact information.

2. What strategies can you use to help you make good choices when you are struggling?

3. What activities are safe for you to do when you're struggling (nothing that would open the door for addictions or dysfunctional behaviors)? Look at the Suggestions for Self Care in the appendices for ideas.

4. What music will help you focus on God rather than the trigger, struggle or addiction? Look at your playlist in Week 7 to help you choose some songs.

5. Where can you be most safe (emotionally, spiritually, physically – your home, someone else's home, a park, library, church, etc.)? What is a safe location for you in your home (bedroom, bathroom, closet, etc.)?

6. What are powerful Scriptures that help you the most in a crisis state?

Comprehensive Action Plan

Category	Your List
Safe People	
Recovery Strategies	
Healthy Coping Skills	
Positive Music	
Safe Places	
Powerful Scriptures	

Emotional Survival Kit
Week 8 Homework

If home or work is where you're unsafe (or where you sometimes feel unsafe), you may need to go somewhere else in order to regroup to get focused or calm your emotions. If that's the case, then your safest grounding place may be outside or the closest available private room or bathroom. At those times, it will be helpful to have an Emotional Survival Kit made up to have on hand quickly. We've made a list of helpful components to have in your Emotional Survival Kit.

- o Backpack or bag of some type
- o Bible
- o A copy of your personal Comprehensive Action Plan Worksheet
- o Copies of any assignments you feel you would be helpful, such as Who God Is scripture list and Who You Are scripture list, etc.
- o Tissues
- o Stress ball, fidget toy
- o Snacks, water
- o First aid kit
- o Coloring book, journal, paper
- o Pen, pencil, crayons or colored pencils
- o Cash, batteries, flashlight, cell phone charging pack
- o Windbreaker, umbrella
- o Snuggly blanket, stuffed animal, comfort toy

Is there anything else you think would be helpful?

Self Care Guide Worksheet
Week 8 Homework

"Self care" is a term we often toss around, but what does it really mean to take care of our-selves? Many think about "self care" as a way of taking care of our body and our soul, but what about our spirit? The following questions will help you create a self care plan that helps you take care of all three parts of your being: spirit, soul, and body. Self care requires intentionality.

First, let's see where you are in your self care. Are you already taking care of your spirit, soul and body?

Spirit:
1. Are you connecting with others that speak life into you?

2. What does your prayer time look like?

3. Are you scheduling time to read your Bible?

4. Are you doing some type of devotional that encourages you?

5. Are you memorizing or meditating on scriptures that speak Truth to you?

Soul:

1. Do you have enough support built into your healthy support system?

2. Who are your trusted friends/support who you can call to talk through problems and concerns with?

3. Are you releasing emotions (crying, exercising, journaling, etc.)?

4. What outlets do you have for creativity?

Body:

1. What do you like to do for fun?

2. Are you getting enough sleep/rest?

3. Are you nourishing your body with nutritious foods?

4. Are you getting a healthy level of exercise?

From the questions above:
1. What can I include in my schedule that will promote a healthy spirit?

2. What can I include in my schedule that will promote a healthy soul (mind, will and emotions)?

3. What can I include in my schedule that will promote a healthy body?

Now that you've had a chance to reflect on your self care habits, you can take the answers you wrote above and add them to the Self Care Guide graphic on the next page. This will help you to see them easily and make sure you are staying balanced and caring for all three areas: spirit, soul, and body. You can also reference the appendices for the Suggestions for Self Care.

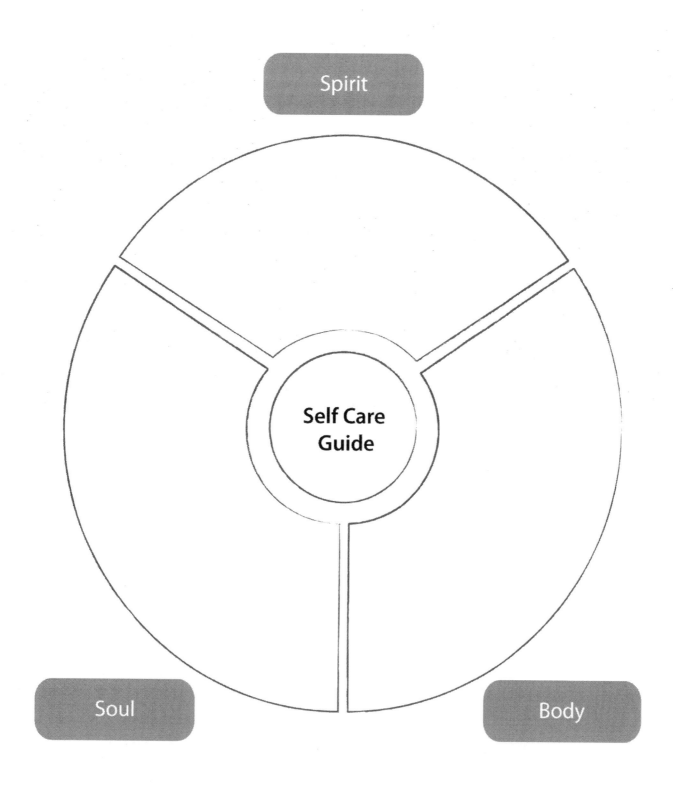

Week 9

Progression of Sin

LISTENING GUIDE

Step #1: _____

Temptations can come as thoughts or images that enter our minds through memories, situations, or literal invitations from others.

Tempting thoughts are not sin. They are only thoughts.

Temptations can arise when we are trying to stop an old pattern or when we are trying to escape a current painful emotion or we are seeking for something to satisfy a need.

Some temptations are directly from the enemy. Others are ripple effects from the hurt and sin in this world. Others are habits due to our past familiarity with this pattern of behavior. Chemical addictions or behaviors that result in hormonal release (exercise, gambling, masturbation, etc.) result in cravings that have a physical component as well as a soul component.

> **Strategy #17**
>
> **Taking Thoughts** _____

NOTES

We can choose to dwell on the tempting thoughts, but it will result in moving closer to the sin.

If we can take those thoughts captive and make them obedient to Christ, replace them with scriptural truth, or leave them at the foot of the cross early on, we can avoid the downward spiral.

In order to take thoughts captive, we need to be aware of our thoughts. This requires us to look inward and examine our thinking on a regular basis.

This is a skill we can develop over time with some intentional focus and help from the Holy Spirit. We get faster at taking temptations captive with practice.

Step #2: Pulled _____

When you spend any amount of time entertaining a temptation in your mind, it is taking up bandwidth and energy that you could be focusing on the things of God.

Your focus is pulled away from God or Jesus and directed toward the sin.

Step #3: _____

As we amass time and energy focusing on the temptation, we begin to feel a desire for what the temptation will bring.

Desires can be sexual, but often they can just be a desire for physical safety, relational safety, love, attention, relief, giving up, numbing, escape, or control.

Step #4: _____

Our imagination begins to come into play and fantasies can begin to play in our mind's eye.

We imagine what it will feel like or how life might be different when the behavior is carried out.

Often, the enticement feels like the only way to solve our pain or current circumstances in the short term. We can rationalize our decisions based on the lie that we need or deserve the behavior while downplaying the consequences.

Step #5: Sin is _____

At this point, we begin to plan how we will carry out the sin and decide to take action.

We may even take steps to prepare for the committing of the sin. If it is a sin we are ashamed of at some level, then we may take steps to ensure we are doing it in secret.

NOTES

Step #6: _____

This is the actual committing out of the sin.

Step #7: _____

Death is always the consequence for sin. This can be an immediate physical death, but more often it is a spiritual and soul wound that leaves us vulnerable.

Since God is the source of life, then any sin we commit reduces our ability to be fully connected and receive life from Him. Instead, we have left ourselves vulnerable to the enemy's lies, which are intended to kill and destroy.

There are consequences to sin. Sometimes, the sin and consequences are tangible, such as alcoholism leading to cirrhosis of the liver. Other times, intangible sin that is not repented of will have physical consequences, such as fear leading to panic attacks or unforgiveness leading to ulcers or cancer.

WEEKLY WORSHIP
"God I Look to You" by Bethel

DISCUSSION QUESTIONS
1. Before watching this week's video, had you ever considered there was a progression of events leading to sin? If not, how does this differ from what you previously thought?

2. How could you use this knowledge to interrupt the progression of sin in your mind after you are tempted?

3. What negative thoughts or lies about yourself have you heard in your mind recently? How would your interactions be different if those negative thoughts were replaced with Biblical truth?

Taking Thoughts Captive Worksheet
Week 9 Homework

We have thousands of thoughts every day based on what we see, how we feel, and who we interact with. Sometimes they happen so fast, we are not consciously aware of the thoughts we are having. This exercise will help you to identify the negative recurring thoughts that are stealing the abundant life God promised and redirect them toward the truth that sets us free.

In the leftmost column, make a list of the negative thoughts you often have about yourself. If you're not sure where to start, you can think about the times when you feel discouraged, disparaged, or beat yourself up in your mind. Or, if you have already identified where you are believing a lie, write down that lie.

In the middle column, write a scripture verse next to each negative thought/lie that disproves or dispels that negative thought/lie. You may find multiple verses that help you.

In the third column restate your negative thought/lie as a positive statement that aligns with the truth found in the scriptures in the middle column.

Use additional paper if you need it. It is helpful to keep this list handy and look back at it often when negative thoughts/lies arise in your mind. You may want to make a copy and place it or hang it up somewhere safe where you will be reminded of the positive truth daily.

Over time, it will become increasingly easier to take the negative thoughts/lies captive and make them obedient to Christ.

Taking Thoughts Captive

Scripture Verse	Positive Truth
Ex. "Even before He made the world, God loved us and chose us in Christ to be holy & flawless in His sight." (Ephesians 1:4, NLT)	Ex. "I am chosen and seen as holy & flawless by God.

Recurring Negative Thought or Lie

Ex. "I am not good enough."

Taking Thoughts Captive

Scripture Verse

Ex. "Even before He made the world, God loved us and chose us in Christ to be holy & flawless in His sight." (Ephesians 1:4, NLT)

Positive Truth

Ex. "I am chosen and seen as holy & flawless by God.

Recurring Negative Thought or Lie

Ex. "I am not good enough."

Taking Thoughts Captive

Recurring Negative Thought or Lie	Scripture Verse	Positive Truth
Ex. "I am not good enough."	Ex. "Even before He made the world, God loved us and chose us in Christ to be holy & flawless in His sight." (Ephesians 1:4, NLT)	Ex. "I am chosen and seen as holy & flawless by God.

Cognitive Distortions

LISTENING GUIDE

Cognitive Distortion #1: All-or-Nothing Thinking

All-or-Nothing Thinking is also known as black-and-white thinking because there is an inability to allow for flexibility or shades of grey between two extremes.
- ○ "If I didn't win, then I am a loser."

Cognitive Distortion #2: Overgeneralization

Overgeneralization is when a broad generalization is made based upon a single event.

Overgeneralizations will often include extreme words to describe a person or situation:
- ○ "She never says anything kind."
- ○ "I never get recognized for my contributions."

Cognitive Distortion #3: Catastrophizing

Catastrophizing is when the worst-case scenario or scenarios are thought of immediately as a realistic threat. This kind of thinking will blow things out of proportion very quickly. It appears as if "the end of the world" is moments away, when, in reality, it has a very small chance of occurring.

NOTES

- "Jennifer in HR didn't smile at me this morning, so I'm probably on the short list to be fired. I'll lose my apartment if I can't find another job. I will probably end up homeless because I refuse to move in with my toxic parents."

Catastrophizing exaggerates the bad while negating the good.
- "I know I just had a pretty good performance review, but Jennifer has never ignored me like that. I should start looking for a new job tonight when I get home so I don't lose my apartment."

Cognitive Distortion #4: Mental Filtering

Although we can receive positive and negative messages all day long, mental filtering will discard the positive feedback and experiences as irrelevant. Instead, the negative thoughts and experiences will seem bigger and more real and important than the positive.

It can be described as a binocular view, where zooming in on the negative experiences leaves no room nor bandwidth for the positive experiences to be embraced.

Often, what is concrete evidence of a positive experience will be dismissed, rather than embraced as proof of a positive encounter.
- "It's nice that my mother-in-law offered to baby sit the kids for free all week, but I still have to prep their meals, pack their bags, do their laundry, get their homework organized, and remember to pay the bills and get the oil changed and prep the guest room for her. The list is endless."

Cognitive Distortion #5: Jumping to Conclusions

Jumping to Conclusions is the tendency to make conclusions and predictions based on little to no evidence. Then, rather than allowing for a range of possible outcomes, one conclusion is decided on and seen as gospel truth.

It is also present when assuming you know what another person is thinking. Often, the view is inaccurate and negative.
- "She didn't do the dishes like she promised; I hate when she gets passive aggressive like this!"
- "He cleaned the kitchen just to make me feel guilty."

Cognitive Distortion #6: Personalization

Personalization involves taking big things and even very small things personally. An assumption is made that most times people make decisions based on their relationship with you above any other factor.

Situations seem to arise because of you or your behavior with no logical reason to believe you are to blame.

NOTES

- "When he canceled our meeting, I knew it was because he was angry about what I had said the day before."
- "She doesn't have to say it out loud; I know she gave the project to someone else because I'm not good enough."

Cognitive Distortion #7: Shoulding or Musting

Shoulding or Musting happens when holding yourself or others to specific expectations. When those expectations aren't met, anger and resentment are the result. Indicators of this kind of distortion are found in the phrasing:
- I "should" do…
- what you "must" do is…
- what you "ought" to do is…
- I "have to" do this…

For example:
- "Company is coming over, so I have to clean the house spotless even though I am sick and overwhelmed."
- "I must do whatever I can to make sure I do not hurt or offend my friends with my opinions, even if I disagree."
- "They ought to spend more time with their children rather than at work. They are going to ruin their children's lives this way. How can they not see that?"
- "They should work overtime or get a second job to provide for their family rather than accepting help from others. That's unacceptable behavior!"

Cognitive Distortion #8: Emotional Reasoning

Emotional reasoning is when a person believes something because they feel like it is true. In these situations, factual proof is not enough to override the emotion or feeling. Reality is based on the overwhelming feeling. They believe if another truth were present, their feelings would be different. There is no allowance for emotions and reality being different from each other.
- "I feel _____ therefore it must be true."
- "I'm scared, so I must be in danger"
- "I feel like a failure, therefore I must be a failure."

Cognitive Distortion #9: Always Being Right

Under the Always Being Right distrotion, one believes they are always correct and accurate. In fact, it is impossible to conceive of a wrong idea or behavior. The idea is offensive. Therefore, an intellectual battle will be launched and pursued until the opposing party concedes or, at the very least, walks away.
- "You're wrong. There is no possible way your point of view is correct. I refuse to try to see it from any other perspective because I already know I'm right."
- "I am going to make sure everyone knows how I am right and how completely wrong they are."

NOTES

Cognitive Distortion #10: Magnification and Minimization

Magnification and Minimization is the tendency to magnify the positive in others while mini-mizing the positive in one's self. Again, facts and physical evidence are dismissed as unimport-ant in framing one's perspective.

- o "She has an amazing life because she has a husband and kids; I just have a career help-ing people and a big paycheck."
- o "He has an amazing life because he has a career that impacts the world and a big pay-check. I just stay home and play homemaker for my spouse and kids."

Change your thoughts – change your results.
Did you know it is possible to step out of these cognitive distortions and change your think-ing? Being armed with the understanding of how these distortions can keep you stuck and frustrated is the first step to helping you identify when you are falling into these distorted thought patterns and perspectives.

The next step is to actively take your thoughts captive and look at how these thoughts will impact your perspective, emotions and actions and, ultimately, what kind of results these thoughts will yield.

For example, if you are caught in the pattern of Shoulding or Musting, you will begin to hold resentments and pull away from those who do not meet your expectations. The results are divisions in relationships, which can lead to elevated stress and possibly isolation.

To change your results, you can change/lower your expectations of others and allow for a difference of behaviors and opinions. Then you will have the opportunity to learn more about why their expectations are different and perhaps build a closer relationship.

WEEKLY WORSHIP
"You Say" by Lauren Daigel

DISCUSSION QUESTIONS
1. What was the most obvious cognitive distortion you recognized as a thought filter you've been using?

2. How have cognitive distortions played a role in your relationships with others?

3. How would your life improve if you responded to life without the cognitive distortion you identified in question 1?

NOTES

Cognitive Distortions Worksheet

Week 10 Homework

Answer the following questions and give examples whenever the answer is "Yes."

1. Do you often label yourself or others as entirely one thing or another, without allowing for more complex explanations?

2. Have you ever assumed that just because a specific result came from a situation the first time, that result always occurs from the same situation or circumstance?

3. When a challenge arises, do you immediately think of the worst-case scenario?

4. Do you focus on the negative events more than the positive events in your life?

5. Do you believe you know what someone else is thinking or will do next?

6. Do you believe others make decisions based on how it will affect you personally?

7. Have you made decisions based solely on what you "should" or "ought" to do?

8. Do you think your feelings are truth, even if you do not have physical proof to back it up?

9. Do you launch into an intellectual battle if someone believes you are wrong?

10. Do you assign more importance to positive events that happen to others, while minimizing similar events when they happen to you?

If you answered "Yes" to any of these questions, then your thinking is subject to one or more Cognitive Distortion.

Mental Health Family Tree Exercise

Week 10 Homework

In this exercise you will draw a diagram of your family tree and the mental diagnoses, conditions, trauma, symptoms, and/or addictions of each person. We list examples below to help guide you through the process and get you started.

To give you enough room, there is a full page provided for each of your parents' families. There is also a sample family tree provided to give you some inspiration. You do not need to include boxes for any category of family member that is not in your family. (For example, you do not need a box for cousins, if you do not have any cousins.)

If you have children and grandchildren, you may include them on either family tree. You are not required to write them twice, but you may wish to do so if you want to see the correlation to each parents' family.

Examples:

Diagnoses:
1. Depression
2. Anxiety Disorder
3. Bipolar
4. PTSD
5. Autism
6. Dementia/Alzheimer's

Trauma:
1. Loss
2. Victim of physical, sexual, emotional, or spiritual abuse
3. Assault, Theft, Fire, Accident, Injury
4. Neglect

Symptoms:
1. Extreme emotional or physical reactions
2. Becoming shut down or withdrawn
3. Sudden changes in personality or temperament
4. Addictions (chemical, sexual, financial, food, codependency, etc.)

Mental Health Family Tree (Sample)
Mother's Side

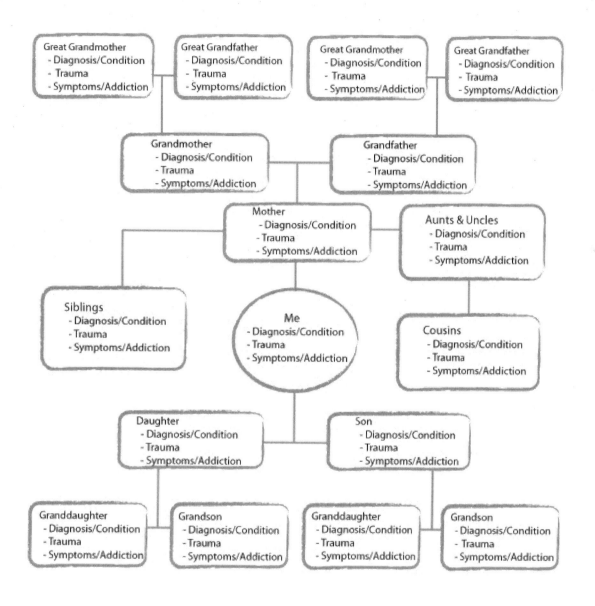

Mental Health Family Tree
Mother's Side

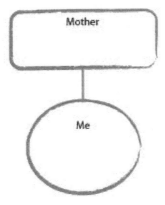

Mental Health Family Tree
Father's Side

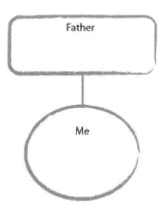

Week 11

Your are NOT
Your Emotions

LISTENING GUIDE

Truth #1: I have emotions. I am not my _____.

Emotions are tools God gave us. They help us to understand the world around us and the thoughts and beliefs in our minds.

Emotions also help us to understand God, who is love, and help us to fully receive grace, mercy, joy, and peace. On the other hand, emotions like anger, jealousy, envy, fear, and sadness can also help us understand when our circumstances or beliefs are more in line with lies than with God's truth.

Emotions do not define us. Emotions are not proof of who God made us to be. Emotions are not sin. Emotions are not part of our DNA. Emotions do not have to control us.

Emotions are always connected to our thoughts or beliefs. If we are feeling an intense emotion, we can more closely examine our thoughts to determine the root cause of the emotion.

Intense emotions can also arise if the current situation reminds us (consciously or unconsciously) of an emotional wound from the past that has not healed.

We do not have to be slave to our emotions and let them control our behavior or attitude. Our emotions do not have to be determined by what is happening around us. We may not be able

NOTES

to choose which emotions arise and when, but we are responsible to choose what we do with them and how we respond in each moment.

Emotions are the thermometer that helps us understand what our emotional thermostat is set to. We can act as our own thermostat and change the intensity or change the emotion by choosing healthy coping mechanisms.

Truth #2: I can't change or get rid of something that I _____ is me.

Sometimes we believe that roles or behaviors or emotions are a part of our DNA or personality, when they are not.

Ways we begin to take on traits that are not part of how God made us include:

- o   Someone told us who they thought we were.
- o   Someone accused us of being the role or behavior.
- o   We believed it was part of us due to how others treated us.
- o   We previously needed the behavior as a coping mechanism and eventually believed it was part of who we were.
- o   We believed it was part of us because we didn't understand that we COULD change our role, behavior, or emotion.
- o   It was often at an early age that we believed the lie about who we were.
- o   We can take off the costume and put down the masks. We can choose to discover who God has made us to be instead.

Truth #3: God _____ us to change.

When we seek after the truth and ask God to empower us from the inside out to be who He made us to be, we can see our decisions and responses begin to change.

This kind of change is not just about creating different behavior on the outside; it is about embracing our identity in Christ more clearly, which will in turn alter our perspectives which will organically change our behavior

Because the Holy Spirit lives inside of us, we can surrender to God and let Him reveal which of our beliefs and behaviors are really part of a costume or mask.

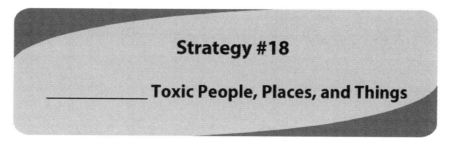

Strategy #18

_____ Toxic People, Places, and Things

It's important to make your home, social network, and daily environment free from temptations so that you will not go back into old behaviors or thought patterns wherever possible.

NOTES

Keeping abusive people in our lives, or staying in abusive situations will only continue to wound you and delay your ability to experience healing and freedom. Toxic people are those whose presence would entice you or influence you to relapse into old patterns. They may intentionally be asking you to rejoin the behavior, or they may be unintentionally tempting you just by living out your old patterns in front of you.

Do not keep items that remind you of the past to the point of tempting you to relapse or stay stuck reliving the past or feeling old emotions. If the temptation to relapse around a person, place, or thing is intense, then it is recommended that you make a hard and immediate boundary with that person, place, or thing.

After you have experienced more healing and developed stronger, healthier coping skills, you may decide later to reintroduce that person, place or thing to your life. Ask for the help of a sponsor, mentor, or professional to determine if that is advisable.

As long as a person or situation is actively abusive, do not allow them any further access to you or your life as far as it is in your power.

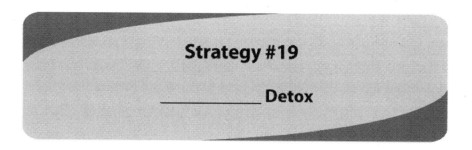

Strategy #19

_____ Detox

WEEKLY WORSHIP
"God Help Me" by Plumb

DISCUSSION QUESTIONS
1. Strategy #18 is remove toxic, people, places and things. Are there people in your life that you need to remove from your bus? Sometimes, a clean break is needed. How would you implement that?

2. Who would you need to put towards the back of your bus? Would you spend less time with them? Give their words less value in your life?

3. To help you become who you want to be, who would you change on your bus?

Toxic Versus Safe Worksheet
Week 11 Homework

We have many people in our lives who affect our direction and well being. To begin to change who we are, we need to address who we allow to influence our lives. To help you understand what changes you may need to make, complete this exercise. On the graphic following, fill out the categories listed below. If a category doesn't apply to your life, leave that category blank. When you are finished, evaluate what changes you need to make in your relationships to make progress toward healing, wholeness and freedom.

Categories:

- Immediate Family--list the 5 people you spend the most time with or energy on
- Work--list the 5 people you spend the most time with or energy on
- Neighborhood--list the 5 people you spend the most time with or energy on
- Church--list the 5 people you spend the most time with or energy on
- Extended Family--list the 5 people you spend the most time with or energy on
- Social--list the 5 people you spend the most time with or energy on

After you have filled out the categories, continue with these steps:

1. Circle the name of the most positive or encouraging person in each category.

2. Cross out the name of the most negative or discouraging person in each category.

3. Now, cross out the names of each person that encourages you in behaviors or thoughts you're trying to avoid or change.

4. Circle the names of the people who encourage you in the direction of seeking God, finding healing, and choosing recovery.

Relational Diagram

Category: _____
1.
2.
3.

    1.
    2.
    3.

Category: _____
1.
2.
3.

    1.
    2.
    3.

Category: _____
1.
2.
3.

    1.
    2.
    3.

Category: _____
1.
2.
3.

    1.
    2.
    3.

Category: _____
1.
2.
3.

    1.
    2.
    3.

Category: _____
1.
2.
3.

    1.
    2.
    3.

Category: _____
1.
2.
3.

    1.
    2.
    3.

Category: _____
1.
2.
3.

    1.
    2.
    3.

NOTES

Unit 1 Assessment

1. Tell us about your support system. Make a list of the people who make up your support team. Then answer these questions about each one.

   a. What role do they play in your life (sponsor, coach, accountability partner, mentor, friend, pastor, etc.)?

   b. How often do you communicate with them?

   c. How has this person been helpful in your healing and recovery so far?

2. What areas have you come out of denial about?
   a. List the areas, then answer the following questions about each area.

    b. What did you think before about this area?

    c. What do you understand about this area now?

3. Do you have a new vision for what recovery or healing may look like for you now? What is your new vision? Describe.

4. Write a paragraph about who you are in Christ. Include the new ways you're learning to see yourself as a child of God.

5. What has changed in how you see God and His heart for you?

6. How did the Father's Repentance and Blessing affect you? Describe. If you utilized the Mother's or Ministry Leader's versions in the appendices, describe how they affected you.

7. How has using the strategy of worship impacted you? Describe.

8. How has your Comprehensive Action Plan and Self Care Guide changed your ability to cope with difficult situations and feelings? Have they helped you make better choices? Describe.

9. What thoughts have you been able to take captive? Have you been having success at replacing the lies with truth more quickly? How have your support people helped you with that? Describe.

10. Have you been having any success recognizing and changing any cognitive distortions? Which ones and how have you changed them?

11. Have you identified people who were doing damage in your life? Have you taken them off your bus or started making a plan to remove them? Explain.

Appendices

Appendix A: Life Events Assessment Answer Key

Congratulations on finishing your Life Events Assessment! That assignment can be very challenging to finish.

To evaluate your assessment, please assign the number next to each answer that you chose. You may circle the same answers on this answer key or use our scoring sheet at the end of this section. You will add all the numbers to get your total. Once you have a total, read our recommendations following the scoring sheet. We want to encourage you as you continue your healing journey.

LOSS (Range 0 to 12)

1. Have you ever experienced a significant loss that affected you physically, emotionally or spiritually?

   Yes – 1

   No – 0

2. Have you ever experienced losing a job that caused emotional/spiritual pain?

   Yes – 1

   No – 0

3. Have you ever experienced the loss of a loved one, a close friend, and/or romantic partner?

   Yes – 1

   No – 0

   a. Was it a sudden death?

      Yes – 1

      No – 0

   b. Did they die by suicide?

      Yes – 1

      No – 0

   c. Was it a violent death?

      Yes – 1

      No – 0

4. Have you ever experienced the death of a child?

   Yes – 1

   No – 0

5. Have you ever experienced the loss of a child to addiction, incarceration, abduction etc.?

   Yes – 1

   No – 0

6. Have you ever experienced a miscarriage?
    Yes – 1
    No – 0
7. Have you ever experienced delivering a stillborn?
    Yes – 1
    No – 0
8. Have you ever been divorced?
    Yes – 1
    No – 0
9. Have you ever had an abortion?
    Yes – 1
    No – 0

STRESSFUL LIFE EVENTS (Range 0-30)

1. Have you ever had a life threatening illness (physical or mental)?
    Yes – 1
    No – 0
2. Do you currently struggle with a chronic illness?
    Yes – 1
    No – 0
3. Have you ever been in a life threating accident?
    Yes – 1
    No – 0
    a. Did anyone die in that accident?
        Yes – 1
        No – 0
    b. Did you sustain serious injuries?
        Yes – 1
        No – 0
4. Have you ever been robbed or mugged?
    Yes – 1
    No – 0
    c. Was physical force or a weapon used?
        Yes – 1
        No – 0
    d. Did you sustain injuries from the event?
        Yes – 1
        No – 0
5. Have you ever been in military combat or a war zone?
    Yes – 1
    No – 0

6. Have you ever witnessed sexual or physical violence?

        Yes – 1

        No – 0

    d. Did it occur before age 10?

            Yes – 3

            No – 0

    e. Did it occur between the ages 10-20?

            Yes – 2

            No – 0

    f. Did it occur after age 20?

            Yes – 1

            No – 0

7. Have you ever witnessed mass violence (riots, shootings, fires, accidents, bombings, etc.)

        Yes – 1

        No – 0

    d. Did it occur before age 10?

            Yes – 3

            No – 0

    e. Did it occur between the ages 10-20?

            Yes – 2

            No – 0

    f. Did it occur after age 20?

            Yes – 1

            No – 0

8. Have you ever witnessed a traumatic natural disaster?

        Yes – 1

        No – 0

9. Have you ever been extremely frightened or horrified, felt helpless or traumatized by a situation that has not been referenced above?

        Yes – 1

        No – 0

10. Have you ever been arrested or been incarcerated?

        Yes – 1

        No – 0

11. Have you ever been in foster care or were you adopted?

        Yes – 1

        No – 0

12. Have you ever lived with anyone who was a problem drinker or alcoholic, and/or used drugs?

        Yes – 1

        No – 0

    e. If you were a child, were your parents too drunk or high to take care of you or take you to the doctor if needed?

        Yes – 1

        No – 0

13. As a child did you ever feel that you didn't have enough to eat, had to wear dirty clothing and/or had no one to protect you?

        Yes – 1

        No – 0

TRAUMA (Range 0 to 107)

1. Have you ever experienced being punched, slapped in the face, hit excessively, kicked, pinned down or otherwise physically attacked or harmed by someone?

        Yes – 2

        No – 0

    f. Did it occur before age 10?

        Yes – 3

        No – 0

    g. Did it occur between the ages 10-20?

        Yes – 2

        No – 0

    h. Did it occur after age 20?

        Yes – 1

        No – 0

    i. Did you sustain injuries?

        Yes – 1

        No – 0

    j. Was it by a spouse or romantic partner?

        Yes – 1

        No – 0

2. Have you ever experienced being repeatedly ridiculed, put down, ignored or told you were worthless, had no value or otherwise verbally attacked or demeaned?

        Yes – 2

        No – 0

    a. Did it occur during ages 0-10?

        Yes – 1

        No – 0

    b. Did it occur during ages 10-20?

        Yes – 1

        No – 0

  c. Did it occur during ages 20 plus?
     Yes – 1
     No – 0
  d. Was it by a spouse or romantic partner?
     Yes – 1
     No – 0

3. Have you ever experienced someone attempting to control or manipulate your emotions by dismissing your feelings, by convincing you your feelings are wrong or improper by making threats etc.
     Yes – 2
     No – 0
  e. Did it occur before age 10?
     Yes – 3
     No – 0
  f. Did it occur between the ages 10-20?
     Yes – 2
     No – 0
  g. Did it occur after age 20?
     Yes – 1
     No – 0
  h. Was it by a spouse or romantic partner?
     Yes – 1
     No – 0

4. Have you ever experienced being physically forced to have intercourse, oral or anal sex against your wishes (even if you were asleep, intoxicated or married to them)?
     Yes – 3
     No – 0
  e. Did it occur before age 10?
     Yes – 3
     No – 0
  f. Did it occur between the ages 10-20?
     Yes – 2
     No – 0
  g. Did it occur after age 20?
     Yes – 1
     No – 0
  h. Was it same gender?
     Yes – 2
     No – 0

5. Have you ever experienced being touched or forced/coerced to touch others inappropriately in private areas (over or under clothing)?

        Yes – 2

        No – 0

    d. Did it occur before age 10?

            Yes – 3

            No – 0

    e. Did it occur between the ages 10-20?

            Yes – 2

            No – 0

    f. Did it occur after age 20?

            Yes – 1

            No – 0

6. As a child, did you experience someone exposing their genitalia or breasts, view pornography, or witness sex of any type?

        Yes – 2

        No – 0

    c. Did it occur before age 10?

            Yes – 3

            No – 0

    d. Did it occur between the ages 10-20?

            Yes – 2

            No – 0

7. As an adult, have you ever experienced someone inappropriately exposing their genitalia or breasts, forcing you to view pornography and/or witness sex of any type?

        Yes – 1

        No – 0

8. Have you ever experienced someone using God, religion, or their spiritual authority to control you, punish you or harm you in anyway?

        Yes – 3

        No – 0

    d. Did it occur before age 10?

            Yes – 3

            No – 0

    e. Did it occur between the ages 10-20?

            Yes – 2

            No – 0

    f. Did it occur after age 20?

            Yes – 1

            No – 0

9. Have you ever been forced/coerced to engage in bestiality?
> Yes – 4
>
> No – 0

> d. Did it occur before age 10?
>> Yes – 3
>>
>> No – 0

> e. Did it occur between the ages 10-20?
>> Yes – 2
>>
>> No – 0

> f. Did it occur after age 20?
>> Yes – 1
>>
>> No – 0

10. Have you ever been forced/coerced to engage in any sexual behavior by anyone for their profit?
> Yes – 4
>
> No – 0

> e. Did it occur before age 10?
>> Yes – 3
>>
>> No – 0

> f. Did it occur between the ages 10-20?
>> Yes – 2
>>
>> No – 0

> g. Did it occur after age 20?
>> Yes – 1
>>
>> No – 0

> h. Was it photographed or filmed?
>> Yes – 2
>>
>> No – 0

11. Have you ever been locked up, caged in, barricaded in a room (basement, closet, shed, etc.) against your will?
> Yes – 2
>
> No – 0

> d. Did it occur before age 10?
>> Yes – 3
>>
>> No – 0

> e. Did it occur between the ages 10-20?
>> Yes – 2
>>
>> No – 0

> f. Did it occur after age 20?
>> Yes – 1
>>
>> No – 0

12. Have you ever experienced being physically, emotionally, or spiritually neglected and/ or abandoned by a parent, loved one or someone you were in close relationship?

>Yes – 2
>
>No – 0

>d. Did it occur before age 10?
>
>>Yes – 3
>>
>>No – 0

>e. Did it occur between the ages 10-20?
>
>>Yes – 2
>>
>>No – 0

>f. Did it occur after age 20?
>
>>Yes – 1
>>
>>No – 0

13. Have you ever been part of a cult?

>Yes – 2
>
>No – 0

>d. Did it occur before age 10?
>
>>Yes – 3
>>
>>No – 0

>e. Did it occur between the ages 10-20?
>
>>Yes – 2
>>
>>No – 0

>f. Did it occur after age 20?
>
>>Yes – 1
>>
>>No – 0

RECOVERY JOURNEY THUS FAR

1. Have you ever completed an inpatient detox/rehab program?

>Yes - 100 brownie points, gold stars, and high fives!
>
>No

2. Have you ever completed an intensive outpatient or partial hospitalization?

>Yes - 100 brownie points, gold stars, and high fives!
>
>No

3. Have you ever spent significant time with a counselor processing your past?

>Yes - 100 brownie points, gold stars, and high fives!
>
>No

4. Have you ever worked through the 12 steps in a recovery group?

>Yes - 100 brownie points, gold stars, and high fives!
>
>No

5. Have you ever worked through an in-depth inner healing program?

>Yes - 100 brownie points, gold stars, and high fives!
>
>No

6. Have you forgiven your abusers or those who have hurt you?
   - Yes - 100 brownie points, gold stars, and high fives!
   - No

7. Are you currently working toward forgiving your abusers or those who hurt you?
   - Yes - 100 brownie points, gold stars, and high fives!
   - No

8. Are you frequently spiritually lifted up by your relationship with God?
   - Yes - 100 brownie points, gold stars, and high fives!
   - No

9. Do you currently have a spiritual and/or recovery mentor or sponsor?
   - Yes - 100 brownie points, gold stars, and high fives!
   - No

10. Do you currently have several safe accountability partners that you can be honest with (without being judged or criticized)?
    - Yes - 100 brownie points, gold stars, and high fives!
    - No

*This tool is not meant to treat or diagnose anyone. It is only a tool to assess the possible impact previous events may have on your present and future.

Recommendations & Scoring Sheet

Now that you have completed the questionnaire, you will add up the score for each of the questions for each individual section by counting the number to the right of each question you marked.

You can evaluate your scores according to the guide below:

Loss (range 0-12)
- If you scored 0-8, we recommend that you have a healthy support system in place as you walk through Recovery Strategies 4 Life.
- If you scored 9-12, we recommend that you have a healthy support system and also work with a professional specializing in grief.

Stressful Life Events Section (range 0-30)
- If you scored 0-10, we recommend that you have a healthy support system in place as you walk through Recovery Strategies 4 Life.
- If you scored 11-30, we recommend that you have a healthy support system and also work with a professional specializing in stressful life events.

Trauma (range 0-107)
- If you scored 0-7, we recommend that you have a healthy support system in place as you walk through Recovery Strategies for Life.
- If you scored 8 or more, we recommend that you have a healthy support system and also work with a professional specializing in trauma.

Recovery Journey Thus Far
Give yourself 100 brownie points, gold stars, and high fives for every question you answered with a "yes!" This isn't a cheesy, fluffy scoring system. The high score is intentional because we know exactly how difficult it is to take steps toward healing.

Each one takes tremendous courage. Even on the days when just breathing and making it through the day was all you could do, you fought through it to the other side. You are a warrior!

Plus, we know that you likely downplay all of the courage and strength you had to muster to accomplish each recovery step. The healing process is messy. It is not a straight line to healing. We will still have hard days even as we heal. That is why we celebrate every "baby step" or "stumble forward."

LOSS (range 0-12)

1. _____
2. _____
3. _____
    a. _____
    b. _____
    c. _____
4. _____
5. _____
6. _____
7. _____
8. _____
9. _____
10. _____
11. _____
12. _____

Score: _____

STRESSFUL LIFE EVENTS (range 0-30)

1. _____
2. _____
3. _____
    a. _____
    b. _____
4. _____
    a. _____
    b. _____
5. _____
6. _____
    a. _____
    b. _____
    c. _____
7. _____
    a. _____
    b. _____
    c. _____
8. _____
9. _____

10. _____
11. _____

Score: _____

TRAUMA (range 0-107)

1. _____
    a. _____
    b. _____
    c. _____
    d. _____
    e. _____
    f. _____
2. _____
    a. _____
    b. _____
    c. _____
    d. _____
    e. _____
3. _____
    a. _____
    b. _____
    c. _____
    d. _____
4. _____
    a. _____
    b. _____
    c. _____
    d. _____
    e. _____
5. _____
    a. _____
    b. _____
    c. _____
    d. _____
6. _____
    a. _____
    b. _____
7. _____
8. _____

    a. _____
    b. _____
    c. _____
    d. _____
9. _____
    a. _____
    b. _____
    c. _____
    d. _____
10. _____
    a. _____
    b. _____
    c. _____
    d. _____
11. _____
    a. _____
    b. _____
    c. _____
    d. _____
12. _____
    a. _____
    b. _____
    c. _____
    d. _____

Score: _____

RECOVERY JOURNEY THUS FAR

1. _____
2. _____
3. _____
4. _____
5. _____
6. _____
7. _____
8. _____
9. _____
10. _____

Score: _____ x 100 = _____

Appendix B: Who We Are Scripture List

I am his friend. (John 15:15)

I am chosen. (John 15:16)

I am complete in Him. (Colossians 2:10)

I am fearfully and wonderfully made. (Psalm 139:14)

I am a new creation. (2 Corinthians 5:17)

I am His workmanship. (Ephesians 2:10)

I am a child of the light. (1 Thessalonians 5:5)

I am a child of the most high! (John 1:12, 1 John 4:4)

I am an heir of God and a joint heir with Christ. (Romans 8:17)

I am more than a conqueror. (Romans 8:37)

I am adopted as God's sons and daughters through Jesus Christ. (Ephesians 1:5)

My body is the temple of the Holy Spirit. (1 Corinthians 6:19)

I am the head and not the tail, I am at the top and never the bottom. (Deuteronomy 28:13)

I am holy. (Ephesians 1:4)

I am a member of the royal priesthood. (1 Peter 2:9)

I am set apart. (Psalm 4:3)

I am totally and completely forgiven. (1 John 1:9)

I am God's intentional and perfectly planned creation. (Psalm 139:13)

Appendix C: Who God Is Scripture List

God is:

Accepting - Romans 15:7
Available - Jeremiah 29:13
Caring - 1 Peter 5:7
Close - Psalm 34:18-19
Comforter - 2 Corinthians 1:3-4
Compassionate - Lamentations 3:22-23
Deliverer - Psalm 18:2
Encouraging - Romans 15:4
Faithful - 1 Thessalonians 5:24
Father - Galatians 4:6
Forgiving - Daniel 9:9
Generous - James 1:17
Giving - John 3:16
Good - Psalm 106:1
Gracious - Ephesians 2:8-9
Healer - Psalm 103:3
Humble - Matthew 11:28-30
Light - Ephesians 5:8
Lord - Acts 10:36
Love - 1 John 4:16
Loyal - Deuteronomy 31:6
Merciful - Psalm 86:15
Mighty - Psalm 24:8
Miracle-worker - Hebrews 2:4

Omnipresent - Psalm 139:7-10
Omniscient - Psalm 139:16
Patient - 2 Peter 3:15
Powerful - Joshua 4:24
Redeemer - Isaiah 34:5
Refreshing - Acts 3:19-20
Refuge - Psalm 46:1, Psalm 91
Restorer - Psalm 23:3
Reviver - Psalm 19:7
Righteous - Psalm 89:14
Rock - Deuteronomy 32:4
Servant - Mark 10:45
Shepherd - Psalm 23:1
Shield - Proverbs 30:5
Sovereign - Daniel 5:21b
Sympathetic - Hebrews 4:15-16
Teacher - Isaiah 28:26
Transformer - 2 Corinthians 5:17
Trustworthy - Deuteronomy 7:9
Truth - John 14:6
Unchangeable - Malachi 3:6
Understanding - Isaiah 40:28
Warrior - Exodus 14:14
Wise - Job 12:13

Appendix D: The Serenity Prayer

By Reinhold Niebuhr

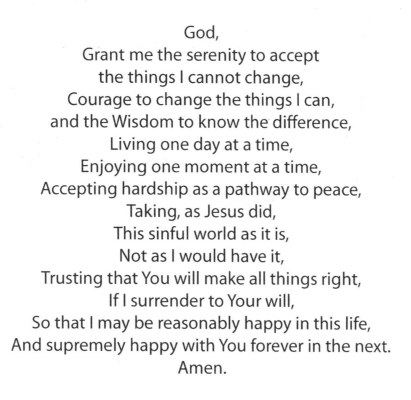

God,
Grant me the serenity to accept
the things I cannot change,
Courage to change the things I can,
and the Wisdom to know the difference,
Living one day at a time,
Enjoying one moment at a time,
Accepting hardship as a pathway to peace,
Taking, as Jesus did,
This sinful world as it is,
Not as I would have it,
Trusting that You will make all things right,
If I surrender to Your will,
So that I may be reasonably happy in this life,
And supremely happy with You forever in the next.
Amen.

Appendix E: Hotlines

General Christian Counseling Services
New Life Clinics: 1-800-NEW-LIFE
National Prayer Line: 1-800-4-PRAYER
Liberty Godparent Ministry: 1-800-368-3336
Grace Help Line 24 Hour Christian Service: 1-800-982-8032
The 700 Club Hotline: 1-800-759-0700
Want to Know Jesus?: 1-800-NEED-HIM
Biblical Help for Youth in Crisis: 1-800-HIT-HOME
Rapha National Network: 1-800-383-HOPE
Emerge Ministries: 330-867-5603
Association of Christian Counselors: 1-800-526-8673

Abortion
National Abortion Federation Hotline: 1-800-772-9100
Post Abortion Counseling: 1-800-228-0332
Post Abortion Project Rachel: 1-800-5WE-CARE

Abuse
National Sexual Assault Hotline: 1-800-656-HOPE (4673)
Stop It Now!: 1-888-PREVENT
United States Elder Abuse Hotline: 1-866-363-4276
Child Abuse Hotline/Dept of Social Services: 1-800-342-3720

Addiction
Families Anonymous: 1-800-736-9805
Drug Abuse National Helpline: 1-800-662-4357
National Assoc. for Children of Alcoholics: 1-888-554-2627
Alcoholics for Christ: 1-800-441-7877

Caregivers
Elder Care Locator: 1-800-677-1116
Well Spouse Foundation: 1-800-838-0879

Chronic Illness/Chronic Pain
Rest Ministries: 1-888-751-REST (7378)

Crisis Numbers for Teens (Under 18)
Girls and Boys Town: 1-800-448-3000
Youth Crisis Hotline: 1-800-448-4663
Covenant House Nineline: 1-800-999-9999

National Runaway Switchboard: 1-800-621-4000
Youth Crisis Hotline: 1-800-448-4663

Crisis Pregnancy Helpline
Crisis Pregnancy Hotline: 1-800-67-BABY-6
Liberty Godparent Ministry: 1-800-368-3336

Cult Information
Cult Hotline (Mercy House): 606-748-9961

Domestic Violence
National Domestic Violence Hotline: 1-800-799-SAFE
National Domestic Violence Hotline (Spanish): 1-800-942-6908
Battered Women and their Children: 1-800-603-HELP
RAINN: 1-800-656-HOPE (4673)
Family Violence Prevention Center: 1-800-313-1310

Eating Disorders
Eating Disorders Awareness and Prevention: 1-800-931-2237
Eating Disorders Center: 1-888-236-1188
National Association of Anorexia Nervosa and Associated Disorders: 1-847-831-3438

Gambling
Compulsive Gambling Hotline: 410-332-0402

Grief/Loss
GriefShare: 1-800-395-5755

Homeless/Shelters
Homeless: 1-800-231-6946
American Family Housing: 1-888-600-4357

Homosexual/Lesbian
Recovery: Exodus International: 1-888-264-0877
Gay and Lesbian National Hotline: 1-888-843-4564
Trevor Hotline (Suicide): 1-866-4-U-TREVOR

Parents
Building Futures: 1-800-A-WAY-OUT
United States Missing Children Hotline: 1-800-235-3535
Missing Children Help Center: 1-800-872-5437

Rape/Sexual Assault
RAINN: 1-800-656-HOPE (4673)

Self-Injury, "Cutting"
S.A.F.E. (Self Abuse Finally Ends): 1-800-DONT-CUT

Sexual Addiction
Focus on the Family: 1-800-A-FAMILY

Suicide
Suicide Hotline: 1-800-273-TALK (8255)
Suicide Prevention Hotline: 1-800-827-7571
Deaf Hotline: 1-800-799-4TTY
NineLine: 1-800-999-9999
Holy Spirit Teenline: 1-800-722-5385
Crisis Intervention: 1-800-673-2496

Appendix F: Additional Resources

The content, information, opinions, and viewpoints contained in these additional resources are solely those of the authors or contributors of such materials. We are not endorsing the authors below, nor have they necessarily endorsed the RS4L course. The books are intended for general informational purposes only.

A More Excellent Way, Dr. Henry Wright

Armor of God Bible Study, Priscilla Shirer

Battlefield of the Mind, Joyce Meyers

Boundaries, Dr. Townsend & Dr. Cloud

Bloom In The Dark: True Stories of Hope and Redemption, Paula Mosher Wallace

Bloom Forward: A Journal to Renew Your Mind, Wallace, Snow, Priz

Bloom Today Workbook, Ginny Priz & Paula Mosher Wallace

The Body Keeps The Score, Bessel Van der Kolk, MD

Captivating, John & Stacey Eldridge

Codependent No More, Melody Beattie

Crazy Love, Francis Chan

Ditch The Drama, Ginny Priz

Do You Know Who I Am, Angela Thomas

Emotions, Dr. Charles Stanley

Safe People, Dr. John Townsend & Dr. Henry Cloud

Unashamed, Christine Caine

Uninvited, Lysa Terkeurst

Walking with God, John Eldridge

Appendix G: Bloom Forward Morning Sheet
(Purchase *Bloom Forward* book on Amazon)

Date ___ / ___ / ___ AM

Three positive words I will
choose to say about myself today:

1. _____

2. _____

3. _____

Things I am grateful for:

1. _____

2. _____

How many hours of sleep have
I gotten in the last 24 hours?

_____

The self-care activity I will do today:

What will I pray for instead of
worry about today?

Today's encouraging verse I will memorize (choose a scripture from appendix & copy):

_____

_____

What music will I listen to today
that will inspire me?

Appendix H: Bloom Forward Evening Sheet

Date ___ / ___ / ___ PM

Things I am grateful for:

1. _____

2. _____

Three positive things I said about myself today:

1.

2.

3.

What did I do well today?

What prayer has God answered or what has He provided today? (tiny or huge)

_____

_____

_____

What worries do I need to give to God?

What beauty did I see around me today?

_____

_____

Who do I need to forgive today?

Appendix I: Father's Repentance and Blessing

As the representative of an earthly father who wasn't available,
didn't know how to express love, abandoned you, abused you, didn't protect you,
just wasn't able to be who you needed him to be, or died,
I want to say I'm sorry.

I'm sorry for not fulfilling my role as a loving father.
I'm sorry for not providing for you, protecting you, or taking care of your heart.
I'm sorry for abandoning you, hurting you, abusing you, or neglecting you.
I'm sorry for not loving you, not showing love to you, or not saying "I love you."
I'm sorry for every way I let you down, wasn't there for you, dismissed or rejected you.
I'm sorry for everything that I put above your wellbeing.

I repent to God for myself and my generations before me.
I repent for my brokenness, my lack of parenting, my weaknesses, and failures.
I repent for every way I followed the enemy and his lies.
I repent for every sin that brought damage or curses on you.
I ask for and accept God's forgiveness.

I want to tell you, "I LOVE YOU!"
You are cherished, loved, lovable, and deserving of love.
I am grateful to God for creating you.
You are fearfully and wonderfully made.
You were made perfectly by God's design.
I am blessed to be your father.

I want to bless you with all of God's richest blessings.
May God bless you and guard you.
May the light of God shine upon you, and may God be gracious to you.
May the presence of God be with you and give you peace.
May you become the parent you desire to become.
May you and your children be strong and healthy.
May the Almighty help you.

May He bless you with blessings from heaven above and the earth beneath.
May the Lord nurture you, feed you, and provide for you abundantly.
May your Heavenly Father teach you, guide you, and give you His wisdom.
May the grace, mercy and peace of our Lord rest on you.
May you trust in the Lord and always run to Him first with every need.
May you be above and not beneath, the head and not the tail.

May you have dominion over everything that is contrary to God.
Cursed be everyone who curses you, and blessed be everyone who blesses you.
May your calling be established, your path be made straight, and your mission successful.
And may you love the Lord with all your soul, mind, and strength and serve Him only.
Be blessed.

Download audio version: https://bloominthedark.org/rs4l/fathers-repentance-and-blessing

Appendix J: Mother's Repentance and Blessing

As the representative of an earthly mother who wasn't available,
Didn't know how to express love, abandoned you, abused you, didn't protect you,
Rejected you, just wasn't able to be who you needed her to be, or died,
I want to say I'm sorry.

I'm sorry for not fulfilling my role as a loving, nurturing mother.
I'm sorry for not cuddling, snuggling, nursing, or playing with you.
I'm sorry for not providing for you, protecting you, or taking care of your heart.
I'm sorry for abandoning you, hurting you, abusing you, or neglecting you.
I'm sorry for not loving you, not showing you the love you needed, or not saying "I love you."
I'm sorry for every way I let you down, wasn't there for you, dismissed or rejected you.
I'm sorry for everything that I put above your wellbeing.

I repent to God for myself and my generations before me.
I repent for my brokenness, my lack of parenting, my weaknesses, and failures.
I repent for every way I followed the enemy and his lies.
I repent for every sin that brought damage or curses on you.
I ask for and accept God's forgiveness.

I want to tell you, "I LOVE YOU!"
You are cherished, loved, lovable, and deserving of love.
I am grateful to God for creating you.
You are gorgeous to me.
You were made perfectly by God's design.
I am blessed to be your mother.

I want to bless you with all of God's richest blessings.
May God bless you and guard you.
May the light of God shine upon you, and may God be gracious to you.
May the presence of God be with you and give you peace.
May you become the parent you desire to become.
May you and your children be strong and healthy.
May the Almighty help you.

May He bless you with blessings from heaven above and the earth beneath.
May the Lord nurture you, feed you, and provide for you abundantly.
May your Heavenly Father teach you, guide you, and give you His wisdom.

May the grace, mercy and peace of our Lord rest on you.
May you trust in the Lord and always run to Him first with every need.

May you be above and not beneath, the head and not the tail.
May you have dominion over everything that is contrary to God.
Cursed be everyone who curses you, and blessed be everyone who blesses you.
May your calling be established, your path be made straight, and your mission successful.
And may you love the Lord with all your spirit, soul, mind, and strength and serve Him only.
Be blessed.

Appendix K: Spiritual Leader's Repentance and Blessing

As the representative of an earthly ministry leader who wasn't available,
Didn't know how to express love, abandoned you, abused you, didn't protect you,
Rejected you, just wasn't able to be who you needed him/her to be, or died,
I want to say I'm sorry.

I'm sorry for not providing a healthy, loving spiritual covering for you.
I'm sorry for not praying for you, protecting you, or taking care of your heart.
I'm sorry for abandoning you, hurting you, abusing you, or neglecting you.
I'm sorry for not loving you, or not showing God's pure love to you.
I'm sorry for every way I let you down, wasn't there for you, dismissed or rejected you.
I'm sorry for every time and way that I didn't surrender to God, listen to Him and obey Him.
I'm sorry for every way I didn't set an example of Jesus's servant heart.

I repent to God for myself and my generations before me.
I repent for my brokenness, my lack of leadership, my weaknesses, and failures.
I repent for every way I followed the enemy and his lies.
I repent for every sin that brought damage or curses on you.
I repent for not providing spiritual covering for you.
I ask for and accept God's forgiveness.

I want to tell you, "I LOVE YOU with God's pure love!"
You are cherished, loved, lovable, and deserving of God's love.
I am grateful to God for creating you.
You were made perfectly by God's design.
I am blessed to be a spiritual leader to you.

I want to bless you with all of God's richest blessings.
May the Holy Spirit fill you to overflowing.
May you receive all the spiritual gifts and blessings God has ordained for you.
May God bless you and guard you and put His hedge of protection around you.
May the light of God shine upon you, and may God be gracious to you.
May the presence of God be with you and give you peace.
May God raise you to full spiritual maturity.
May you become the spiritual leader you desire to become.
May you lead others with God's heart for healing and redemption.
May the Almighty help you.

May He bless you with blessings from heaven above and the earth beneath.
May the Lord nurture you, feed you, and abundantly provide for you and your family.
May your Heavenly Father teach you, guide you, and give you His wisdom.
May the grace, mercy and peace of our Lord rest on you.
May you trust in the Lord and not in your own understanding.
May you always run to God first with every need.

May you be above and not beneath, the head and not the tail.
May you have dominion over everything that is contrary to God.
Cursed be everyone who curses you, and blessed be everyone who blesses you.
May your calling be established, your path be made straight, and your mission be successful.
And may you love the Lord with all your spirit, soul, mind, and strength and serve Him only.
Be blessed.

Appendix L: Worship Playlist

Lesson Name	Song	Artist
What to Expect	"Freedom Hymn"	Austin French
Saying Hello to Reality	"No Longer Slave"	Bethel
Fantasy vs Reality	"We Believe"	Newsboys
Who God Is	"Who You Say I Am"	Hillsong
God's Heart for Restoration	"Mended"	Matthew West
The Love of Father God	"Fierce"	Jesus Culture
Surrender to God	"I Surrender"	Hillsong
Positive Coping Tools	"Tremble - Live"	Mosaic MSC
Progression of Sin	"God I Look To You"	Bethel
Cognitive Distortions	"You Say"	Lauren Daigle
You Are NOT Your Emotions	"God Help Me"	Plumb

Appendix M: Armor of God Scripture

Ephesians 6:10-18 (NKJV)

"Finally, my brethren, be strong in the Lord and in the power of His might. Put on the whole armor of God, that you may be able to stand against the wiles of the devil. For we do not wrestle against flesh and blood, but against principalities, against powers, against the rulers of the darkness of this age, against spiritual *hosts* of wickedness in the heavenly *places*. Therefore take up the whole armor of God, that you may be able to withstand in the evil day, and having done all, to stand.

Stand therefore, having girded your waist with truth, having put on the breastplate of righteousness, and having shod your feet with the preparation of the gospel of peace; above all, taking the shield of faith with which you will be able to quench all the fiery darts of the wicked one. And take the helmet of salvation, and the sword of the Spirit, which is the word of God; praying always with all prayer and supplication in the Spirit, being watchful to this end with all perseverance and supplication for all the saints."

Download the audio version at: https://bloominthedark.org/rs4l/armor-of-god

Appendix N: Suggestions for Self Care

Walking
Biking
Swimming
Running
Kayaking
Aerobics
Weight Lifting
Group Fitness Class
Massage
Facials

Bathing
Showers
Hot Tub
Pedicure
Manicure
Spa Day
Night with Friend
Concerts
Movies
Netflix/Amazon Prime

Dinner Out
Coffee Date
Sporting Events
Sightseeing
Read a Book
Painting
Coloring
Drawing
Crafting
Hobbies

Add your own ideas:

Appendix O: RS4L Strategies

Unit 1: Relationship With God

	Lesson Title	Strategy
Week 1	What To Expect	#1 – Be Honest With Yourself #2 – Recovery is a Journey Not a Destination #3 – Baby Steps
Week 2	Saying Hello to Reality	#4 – Healthy Support System #5 – Make Changes to Face Reality
Week 3	Fantasy Versus Reality	#6 – Grace for Realistic Recovery #7 – Progress Not Perfection
Week 4	Who God Is	#8 – Understanding Your Intrinsic Value
Week 5	God's Heart for Restoration	#9 – God Can Restore As If Never Broken
Week 7	Surrender to God	#10 – Putting on the Armor of God #11 – Worship
Week 8	Positive Coping Tools	#12 – Emotional Scheduling #13 – Prayer & Meditation #14 – Gratitude #15 – Bilateral Processing #16 – Self-Care
Week 9	Progression of Sin	#17 – Taking Thoughts Captive
Week 11	You are NOT your Emotions	#18 – Remove Toxic People, Place, Things #19 – Emotional Detox

Unit 2: Healing Strategies

Week 12	Fullness of the Holy Spirit	#20 – Fullness of the Holy Spirit
Week 14	Good GRIEF!	#21 – Healthy Grieving
Week 15	Damaging Pain vs Healing Pain	#22 – Physical Release
Week 17	The Real Me	#23 – Who Am I? #24 – Recognizing & Replacing Lies
Week 18	Eternal Perspective	#25 – Eternal Perspective #26 – Tree of Life versus Death
Week 19	What Motivates You?	#27 – Motivation #28 – Scripture #29 – Obedience
Week 20	Healthy Boundaries	#30 – Healthy Boundaries #31 – Remember Whose Opinion Matters
Week 21	Learning to Stabilize	#32 – Grounding #33 – Processing

Unit 3: Healing From The Past

Week 26	Diving Deep	#34 – Identifying Triggers #35 – Identifying Flashbacks #36 – Identifying Dissociation

Unit 4: Claiming Your Freedom

Week 39	Unfair Grace	#37 - Forgiveness
Week 42	Get Into The Ring	#38 – Facing Your Goliath
Week 45	Celebrate	#39 - Celebrating

Unit 5: Walking In Freedom

Week 46   Daily Course Correction   #40 – Course Correct

Week 48   Leveling Up   #41 – Leveling Up

Week 49   Ex-Victim   #42 – Ex-Victim
        #43 – Your New Identity

Week 51   Staying Free   #44 – Serve

Week 52   Walking In Freedom   #45 – Walk in Freedom

Appendix P: Listening Guide Answer Keys

Week 1 Listening Guide

Strategy #1: Be **HONEST** with yourself

Strategy #2: Recovery is a **JOURNEY** not a destination

Strategy #3: **BABY** Steps

Week 2 Listening Guide

Strategy #4: Healthy **SUPPORT** system

Component #1: **SAFETY**

Component #2: **PEOPLE**

Component #3: **RESOURCES**

Question #1: Where do I feel **STUCK?**

Question #2: Do I have recurring **HURTS?**

Strategy #5: Make Changes to **FACE** reality

Consequence #1: **SEPARATES** us from God, ourselves, and others

Consequence #2: **DISABLES** our feelings

Consequence #3: Keeps us stuck and stops **GROWTH**

Week 3 Listening Guide

Factor #1: **DAMAGED** emotional growth plate

Factor #2: Type, severity, or length of **DAMAGE**

Factor #3: **AMOUNT** of investment and effort

Strategy #6: Grace for **REALISTIC** Recovery

Strategy #7: **PROGRESS** Not Perfection

Fantasy #1: **CONTROL** Fantasy

Fantasy #2: "**IF ONLY**" Fantasy

Fantasy #3: **EXPECTATIONS** Fantasy

Fantasy #4: **PRIDE** Fantasy

Week 4 Listening Guide

Part #1: **TRIUNE** Being

Part #2: **GOD'S** Nature

Part #3: Intentional **DESIGN**

Strategy #8: Understanding your intrinsic **VALUE**

Week 5 Listening Guide

Truth #1: God can **REDEEM** us.

Truth #2: God wants to **RESTORE** us.

Strategy #9: God can **RESTORE** as if never broken

Truth #3: **MIRACULOUS** healing is available

Week 6 Listening Guide

Reason #1: **DISTORTS** your view of God

Reason #2: Creates **SEPARATION**

Reason #3: The father wound **DAMAGES** your spirit, soul, and body

Comparison #1: God's **PERFECT** love versus human love

Comparison #2: God's **JUSTICE** versus flawed discipline

Comparison #3: God's consistent **PRESENCE** versus human absence

Comparison #4: God's **ADOPTION** versus human abandonment

Reason #1: **ACCURATE** view of God

Reason #2: Creating **UNITY**

Reason #3: **HEALS** you spirit, soul, and body

Week 7 Listening Guide

Step #1: **CHOOSE** to let Him

Step #2: Not **RELYING** on your own ideas

Step #3: **ACCEPTING** the things you cannot change

Strategy #10: Put on the **ARMOR** of God

Strategy #11: **WORSHIP**

Week 8 Listening Guide

Strategy #12: Emotional **SCHEDULING**

Strategy #13: **PRAYER** & Meditation

Strategy #14: **GRATITUDE**

Strategy #15: Bilateral **PROCESSING**

Strategy #16: **SELF-CARE**

Week 9 Listening Guide

Step #1: **TEMPTATION**

Strategy #17: Taking Thoughts **CAPTIVE**

Step #2: Pulled **AWAY**

Step #3: **LUST**

Step #4: **ENTICEMENTS**

Step #5: Sin is **CONCEIVED**

Step #6: **SIN**

Step #7: **DEATH**

Week 10 Listening Guide (no blanks)

Week 11 Listening Guide

Truth #1: I have emotions. I am not **MY EMOTIONS**

Truth #2: I can't change or get rid of something that I **BELIEVE** is me

Truth #3: God **EMPOWERS** us to change

Strategy #18: **REMOVE** toxic people, places, and things

Strategy #19: Emotional **DETOX**

About Bloom In The Dark, Inc.

Using the fertilizer of our past to bloom!

Have you ever experienced a hurt so deep that it didn't qualify for a sympathy card? Did embarrassment or shame keep you from getting help or support? Do you have a loved one who's been abused?

Many women face trauma and abuse. But that doesn't have to be the end of the story. Countless women have healed from their past with God's power.

Every success story has one thing in common – hope!

We at Bloom In The Dark have seen the power of story provide the kind of hope that change lives!

Mission:

We are a 501c3 charity seeking to raise awareness about the damage caused by secret pain and abuse, and demonstrate the hope and healing found in Christ Jesus through ex-victim testimonies, connections, and tools.

Vision:

To create a culture where people choose redemption and healing in Christ Jesus so they bloom despite darkness and pain.

Values:
- LOVE: Love God, Love yourself so you can Love your neighbor
- HONESTY: Be honest with God, yourself and others especially when it hurts
- FORGIVENESS: Forgive God, yourself and others quickly
- ENCOURAGEMENT: Encourage yourself with God's Word, your words, and other's words through what you see, hear, and speak.

Learn More:
https://bloominthedark.org

Watch Bloom Today TV Around the World

Using the fertilizer of our past to bloom today!

Ephesians 5:8-13 (NIV)
"For you were once darkness, but now you are light in the Lord. Live as children of light (for the fruit of the light consists in all goodness, righteousness and truth) and find out what pleases the Lord. Have nothing to do with the fruitless deeds of darkness, but rather expose them. It is shameful even to mention what the disobedient do in secret. But everything exposed by the light becomes visible—and everything that is illuminated becomes a light."

Television:
(Check your local listings)

Inspiration TV - INI (UK, Europe, Africa, Asia, The Caribbean, New Zealand, & Australia)
Faith USA (USA)
NRB TV (USA)
Upliftv (USA)
CTN (USA)
Alpha Omega (Romania, Moldova)
Grace Television (India)
Australia Christian Channel (Australia)
Family 7 (The Netherlands)
Flow Africa (Kwesé Channel, Africa)
Faith Africa (South Africa)
Faith Terrestrial (Eastern Cape South Africa)
Faith UK (UK)
WHTN (Middle TN)
Sacramento Faith TV (Sacramento, CA)

Online Streaming:

Amazon Prime
Parables
Inspiration TV App
Faith Broadcasting Network App

Global 7 App
Damascus Roads
NRB TV App
Grace TV App

Podcast:
iTunes
iHeartRadio
YouTube
Spreaker
Sonos

Learn More:

https://bloomtodaytv.com

Our Books

Find healing resources,
crisis resources, and
download your FREE copy of

at

Bloominthedark.org/free-book

by
Paula Mosher Wallace
President of Bloom In The Dark, Inc.
paula@bloominthedark.com

A journal to renew your mind...
one day at a time.

Use this 90 day devotional journal with
assessments and daily questions will help
you build new thought patterns,
muscle memories, and neural pathways.

Videos & Coaching Tools
by
Ginny Priz & Paula Mosher Wallace
Based on the Bloom Today TV show

BloomTodayTV.com

Life is messy, but you don't have to be drawn into
all the soul-sucking drama!

Learn how as Ginny Priz unpacks the
Serenity Prayer in her book

Ditch The Drama

Learn more at
ditchthedrama.net

Made in the
USA
Lexington, KY